The Penguin Book of
Twelve Very Short Stories

by

Alan Maley

PENGUIN BOOKS

Published by the Penguin Group
Penguin Books Ltd, 27 Wrights Lane, London w8 5TZ, England
Penguin Books USA Inc., 375 Hudson Street, New York, New York 10014, USA
Penguin Books Australia Ltd, Ringwood, Victoria, Australia
Penguin Books Canada Ltd, 10 Alcorn Avenue, Toronto, Ontario, Canada M4V 3B2
Penguin Books (NZ) Ltd, 182–190 Wairau Road, Auckland 10, New Zealand

Penguin Books Ltd, Registered Offices: Harmondsworth, Middlesex, England

Published by Penguin Books 1995
1 3 5 7 9 10 8 6 4 2

Filmset by Datix International Limited, Bungay, Suffolk
Printed in England by Clays Ltd, St Ives plc
Set in 10.5/12.5 pt Monophoto Plantin

Contents

Introduction

There comes a certain point in learning a foreign language when we feel that we need to become more independent; to strike out on our own, to take more responsibility for our own learning. What is the best way of doing this? Of course, there is no single best way. We all have our own preferences.

Reading is definitely one of the best ways of developing our command of a language. When we read, we can choose what to read (from newspapers to Shakespeare's sonnets), when to read (over breakfast, on holiday, on the train on the way to work, late at night in bed . . .) and how to read (studying the text, looking up every word, or for the sheer pleasure of understanding the story).

However, until we are really confident in the language, most of us are put off by the idea of having to read 'great' literature or even full-length novels. What we want is something we can enjoy and understand, at the same time as learning something from it.

That is what this selection of twelve short stories aims to provide. The stories are intended:

- to be interesting in their own right: the sort of thing you might decide to read even in your own language
- to be short enough to finish in one go. They are all about 1600 words in length

- to contain useful, idiomatic, everyday language at about the right level of difficulty
- to offer some help with more difficult words or expressions. Also to provide a few simple language practice exercises, which will make you go back to the story and read parts of it again, for reinforcement.

In this collection, the stories are about a range of people in situations which are thought-provoking. What would you have done in similar situations? Life is stranger than fiction; perhaps – but all these stories are based, in one way or another, on life. I hope you will enjoy reading them.

Alan Maley

At Your Service

On 15 September Madame Desjardins finally decided to open the room. It was a difficult decision.

Their marriage was based on non-interference in each other's affairs. They had lived under the same roof for twenty years but their lives had been separate. She had had her circle of friends who shared her passion for music. In the winter she spent most evenings at the Opéra or in the Salle Pleyel with one of her many artistic friends. Afterwards they would have dinner in one of the fashionable restaurants off the Champs-Élysées. When she returned home in the early hours of the morning, Edouard would be asleep in his bedroom.

He had a fixed routine. He would get up at six and do some yoga exercises. After that, he had his breakfast. This usually consisted of fresh fruit, croissants and coffee. Madeleine, their maid, would serve it on the dot of seven. In the summer months he would eat on the terrace; in winter in the small dining-room overlooking the garden. He would then bathe, dress in one of his dark, formal suits and walk round the corner to the Parc Monceau. After a brisk walk in the park, he would return home, stopping at the small 'café tabac' on the corner to buy *Le Monde*. By then it would be eight-thirty. He would spend the next hour and a half reading the newspaper. At ten, he would leave the house and make his way to the Bibliothèque Nationale. For many years he had been doing research into the Bushmen tribes of the Kalahari desert. The staff in the library knew him well. They were used to the odd clicking sounds he sometimes made while he was reading. (The Bushmen languages use a lot of clicking sounds.) He was a regular visitor. The library staff made sure that no one else ever sat in his seat near the window. He was a respected scholar, even if he was a bit odd.

Madame Desjardin's first name was Eloise. She usually got up as soon as her husband left the house. This was not done consciously. She did not dislike her husband. It was just that, when he was in, the air felt heavy. Once he had gone out, she felt as if a weight had been lifted from the house. She would then rise. She would never hurry. Madeleine would serve her coffee and croissants in her bedroom. She would then spend an hour or two bathing, deciding on which of her many dresses she would wear, nibbling her croissants and telephoning her friends. They would exchange the latest gossip. This was far more amusing than reading a newspaper, and much less tiring.

Her day really began with lunch. Usually she would eat with one of her female friends. They would go to the Tour d'Argent, or another fashionable restaurant. Apart from the food which, of course, had to be first class, the place had to be 'amusing', 'charming' or 'original'. She and her network of 'friends' were dedicated to amusement. They thought that the world existed in order to provide them with amusement. They called each other by 'fun' names – Mimi, Mado, Aggie, Popol and so on. Her own name had been shortened to Elo.

After lunch she might visit a new exhibition – or call on her beautician, or her *coiffeuse* to make sure that her hair would be in perfect condition for the evening's entertainments.

2

In the evenings, Edouard would return to eat his supper alone. He would then go up to his 'den' on the top floor of the house. No one was allowed inside the room, which he kept locked. Eloise did not know what he did there. She assumed that it must be connected with his clicking Bushmen. Anyway she was too busy, amusing herself, to care.

Their year also followed a regular routine. From September to April they stayed in Paris – he in the library, she at her concerts and restaurants. They would give a supper party at Christmas for the few surviving family members. This was the only social event they shared; their one concession to conventional family life. In the spring, Eloise would spend a month staying with friends who had a villa on a Greek island. She would then move from friend to friend around the continent of Europe, from one 'amusing' location to another, returning to Paris at the end of July.

She would spend the month of August in Paris. This was an odd thing to do, since most Parisians leave on holiday during August to escape from the heat. Eloise, however, thought that it was 'original' to stay in Paris when everyone else had left. It was as if the city was empty. For a whole month it belonged to her alone. It was also the only time when she had the house entirely to herself.

For the past fifteen years Edouard had left Paris on 31 July and returned on 1 September. He would return each year in an exceptionally good mood. Then he would go back to his old routine as if he had never been away. He never offered to explain where he had been, nor what he had been doing. Eloise never asked. She occasionally wondered if he had a mistress somewhere. It seemed unlikely. It would have made no difference anyway.

But this year, he had not returned on 1 September.

3

Two weeks had passed, and still he had not come back. Eloise finally decided she should open the room on the top floor. Perhaps she would find a clue to her husband's disappearance. She waited until Madeleine's evening off. Then she made her way up the narrow wooden stairs leading to the top floor. She had found a large screwdriver, a hammer and a pair of pincers, though she had never in her life had to use tools. It was dark in the corridor, and it took her almost half an hour to prise open the door.

The room was small and airless. It contained a desk, a wardrobe, a bookcase and narrow camp-bed. The floor boards were bare. On the desk there was an address book and a photograph album. In the wardrobe hung a black suit with a swallowtail jacket. Below it was a pair of shiny black patent-leather shoes. There was an odd assortment of books in the bookcase: glossy coffee-table books on some of the great houses and palaces of Europe, guidebooks, a number of dictionaries and phrase books in French, English, Italian, Spanish and German, books on wine and food, and a few volumes on etiquette and manners.

She opened the address book. It contained names of well-known rich, well-connected people from all over the world. There was a well-known Italian businessman with a fabulous villa on Lake Maggiore, a Gulf sheikh famous for his stable of race-horses, a lord with a castle in Scotland, a film actor with a ranch in Texas ... It was incredible. Her own group of friends were nothing by comparison. Did Edouard really know all these people? And if so, how?

She began to look through the photo album. It too contained some surprises. On every page there were pictures of famous faces, taken at receptions and dinner parties. She took one out. On the back there was a

4

dedication. 'From SzaSza to Henri with gratitude for
everything you have done.' She took another, 'Dear Gustave – we'll always remember you. Come again next year.
Yours Sophia.' Every one she looked at contained similar
messages addressed to Michel, Bertrand, Thomas, Claude   135
– as well as to Henri and Gustave. She felt confused and
angry. Why had he never told her? But was this all true,
or was it a sort of fantasy world he had invented during
all those lonely evenings while she had been out? And
who were Henri, Gustave and all the others? And where   140
was he now? She decided to sleep on it, took two sleeping
pills and went to bed.

The letter arrived the next morning. Madeleine
brought it in on the breakfast tray. It had been posted in
Australia. She recognized his spidery writing and tore   145
open the envelope impatiently.

Dear Eloise,

   I am sorry if I have caused you any concern, though I think
that is unlikely. As you can see, I am in Australia, but I shall
be moving elsewhere soon.   150

   I have decided to leave you. I am sure it will not matter very
much to you. Our 'marriage' has never been more than a
matter of convenience. I have made very generous financial
arrangements and transferred the house to you, so you will be
able to continue your usual life-style.   155

   If anyone asks where I am, just tell them that I have gone to
southern Africa to continue my research on the Bushmen. *Do
not* try to trace me. Over the past few years I have found that I
have a gift for service. I now intend to make service my full-
time occupation.   160

   With my best wishes for your future life. I hope you will
find it 'amusing'.

   Yours,
      Edouard.

165 Five years later Eloise visited California with some of her
more amusing friends. One evening they were invited to
a dinner party at the mansion of a famous film magnate,
up in the hills behind Los Angeles. They had gathered
on the terrace for drinks. An elegantly dressed butler in a
170 black swallowtail coat carried in a tray. He passed from
guest to guest discreetly offering them drinks from the
tray. 'Charles was a real discovery,' confided the magnate
to the guests around him, 'He really understands what
service is.' At this point Charles the butler came to a halt
175 in front of Eloise and held out the tray. 'At your service
Madame,' he said, 'I think you will find the Californian
Chardonnay to your taste – an "amusing" little wine.'
And he winked. She fainted. It was Edouard.

Campbell's Crossing

It happened in the year of the great flood and the big freeze. First came the rain. It had started to rain at the end of November and it went on raining more or less without stopping till Christmas. The rivers rose until they flooded the low-lying land along their banks. Glen Lochie was badly affected by the flooding. The bridge at Inverlochie was washed away in mid-November. That meant that the people with crofts and farms on the north side of the river were more or less cut off. It was just possible to get across the river by boat – but terribly dangerous.

Colin Campbell made two trips before Christmas to bring back supplies for himself and the two crofts up on Ben Dun. The second time his small boat almost capsized as it came in. The Campbell farm lies way back from the river but, during the floods, the river came almost up to the farmhouse itself.

Inverlochie was the only village for miles, and very isolated. The three of them had grown up there together. Colin Campbell's father had a farm down in the valley. Angus McLeod lived up on the mountain on a small sheep croft, alone with his father. His mother had died when he was a baby. And Flora lived in the village itself. Her father, James McIntosh, ran the post office and the small general store.

25   The three of them were the same age and became close friends. They did all the things that naughty children do in school. After school they would go up the glen together and pretend that they were outlaws being hunted by the hated British soldiers. Or sometimes the two boys would
30 attack the ruined castle on the hill to rescue Flora from her captors.

    As she grew older, Flora became more and more beautiful. By the time she was fifteen, she was very striking. She had fine white skin and thick red hair. When she
35 walked in the streets of the town on market days all the heads would turn.

    It was obvious that both Colin and Angus were hopelessly in love with her, even then. They still went around as a threesome but there was now a growing rivalry
40 between the two boys.

    Gradually Angus and Flora started to spend much more time together. They were both great readers. He took to studying with her in the back room at the post office after school, before making his way back up to the
45 croft. They would walk together on Sunday afternoons after kirk. Colin sulked. He began to spend his free time alone. He would set off early with his fishing rod and only return late in the evening. He stopped seeing Flora. If he saw Angus coming, he would turn away.

50   By the time they were eighteen, Flora and Angus were inseparable. They were always together. Everyone in Inverlochie expected them to get married. Colin had lost the contest.

55 In his last year at school, Angus won a scholarship to St Andrews University. In the four years he was away he wrote to Flora once a week and told her everything about his new life. She kept him up to date with affairs back in Inverlochie. They spent the vacations together. In his

final year he proposed to her. They were engaged to be married the following year. They were just twenty-one years old. 60

Colin stayed on in the glen when he left school. He took over the family farm when his father died. He rarely went into the village and avoided all contact with Flora. 65

The summer they were due to marry, Angus told Flora that he'd been offered a research fellowship at Harvard. It was something he could not refuse. It would mean postponing their marriage for at least another year. Flora was very upset by it but she loved him very much, so 70 eventually she agreed. He left in September of that year – and that was the last she saw of him for ten years.

Who knows what goes on in people's heads? Or in their hearts? We think we know someone, then suddenly they do something completely unexpected. So it was with 75 Angus. For the first six months he wrote to Flora as regularly as ever. Then the letters came less and less frequently, until they finally stopped. Flora tried to hide her feelings but it was obvious that she was suffering terribly. 80

People tried to cheer her up but some wounds cannot be healed. Then, one Saturday night a few months later, Colin met Flora at a 'ceilidh' in Killiecrachan. Her parents had taken her there. She had gone unwillingly. Who knows exactly what happened between Flora and Colin 85 that evening? Perhaps it was the dancing, or the fiddle music, or the whisky . . . who knows? Anyway, from then on they began to go about together, and within a year they were married. Miss Flora McIntosh became Mrs Flora Campbell. She moved into the farm across the 90 river and began a new life.

They seemed to be happy together. Flora was a good support to Colin and he was full of attention for her.

They never had any children but perhaps children are not everything in a marriage.

Life went on like this for the next nine years. Perhaps it would have continued too, if Angus's father hadn't died. He was a grand old man but he loved his whisky, and one day he went to bed after drinking too much – and never woke up. It was Colin who found him the next morning. He and Flora had taken care of the old man since Angus had gone away. They would pass by most days to see if he needed anything. Angus was working at a university in California by then. Forty-eight hours later he was home – for the first time in ten years.

Everyone went to the funeral down in Inverlochie. The old man had been well liked and respected. The McLeod croft was too small and too remote to receive so many people. So afterwards everyone went back to the Campbell farm for refreshments. It felt strange. There was the embarrassment of the old relationship between Flora and Angus. You could almost feel the electricity in the air. But everything passed off well. Angus said little. Flora smoothed away any awkwardness with her quiet dignity and charm. Colin was courteous and considerate towards Angus. In the end it was almost like old times.

Angus stayed a few days to put his father's affairs in order, then returned to the States. Before leaving, however, he went down to Glasgow to visit Strathclyde University. They offered him a professorship. He accepted it, and a year later he was back. He moved back into his father's croft and commuted from there to Glasgow on weekdays.

Sometimes he and Colin would go fishing at weekends. Occasionally he would have supper with the Campbells down at the farm by the river. Life seemed to have come back to normal again. And it had – until the great flood, and the big freeze that followed it. Who knows, perhaps it would have happened anyway but it was the flood which caused it. 130

It was Christmas Eve. At midday the rain stopped and, for the first time in weeks, the sun came out. By mid-afternoon the floodwaters seemed to be slowly subsiding. The river was still running very fast though. Colin in-sisted on taking the boat across the river to fetch the 135 Christmas mail and to greet his mother. She had moved to the village when they married. Flora was not happy to see him go, but he insisted. He promised to be back before nightfall. Only a fool would have tried to cross in the dark. 140

At five o'clock Angus arrived at the farm, bringing gifts for the Campbells. Flora asked him to stay till Colin returned. He would surely not be long. It was the first time they had been alone together for over ten years. Who knows what they said to each other? We can only 145 imagine. At five o'clock it was already dark. Colin had not come back. Six o'clock came and went, then seven, then eight. Flora kept going to the window to look out for the returning boat – but no boat came. Angus could not leave Flora alone. He stayed on with her. They ate 150 supper together. The night wore on and still Colin did not return.

No one knows what happened between Angus and Flora that night. The feelings men and women have for each other are a mystery. But Angus did not leave the 155 farm until the next morning.

Colin had still not returned. Overnight the great flood had become the big freeze. The grass and trees were covered with glistening hoar frost. The ground was frozen hard. Angus walked towards the water's edge. The flood 160 had receded. The Campbell boat had been hauled up well out of the water. A set of footprints, frozen hard into the mud, led from the boat to the bedroom window. They came to a stop outside the window. Another set of frozen prints, made by the same boots, led back to the water. They disappeared in the ice which was rapidly covering the open water.

They found Colin's body three days later. It was stiff with ice, caught in the debris by the remains of the bridge. His eyes were frozen wide open.

Keep It Dark

I had left early from Cambridge. By lunchtime I had reached Newcastle. My friend Clive was expecting me at Scarfell Place by about five. So I had plenty of time. For the first time since I'd come on leave two weeks before, I had a delicious feeling of total relaxation. Here I was in my old sports car, with no responsibilities except to get to Scarfell by tea time. And no one to please but myself. I had the whole afternoon to drive the forty miles or so to the house (if Clive's directions were accurate, that is). I decided to take the coast road as far as Alnwick and then to turn inland towards the moors.

Going north from Newcastle I felt I'd crossed some sort of psychological frontier. I remembered that this was the historical borderland between England and Scotland – which had been fought over for centuries. I saw in my mind's eye the names on those maps in the old primary school history books: Picts, Scots, Danes ... After the Viking invasion it had been part of a Danish kingdom stretching from York to the Scottish border.

I drove along the coast in the May sunshine. I imagined battles taking place on the beaches – the rocks soaked with blood, heads rolling in the waves. Occasionally I passed the ruins of castles on the cliffs overlooking the sea.

I was getting along so well that I decided to stop for a

walk along the shore. But before I could do so, a thick mist suddenly rolled in off the sea. I could only see a few yards ahead. I had to slow down to a crawl. Luckily, after about a mile, I came to a small fishing village. I

30 parked and got out of the car. The place was empty. There were the faint shapes of one or two fishing boats in the tiny harbour but no people.

I decided to have my walk anyway. Perhaps the mist would lift. I followed a footpath sign to 'Calnwick Castle.

35 Ancient Monument. 1 Mile.' The mist had cut off the sun entirely and it was both gloomy and cold. I began to doubt my own senses: my eyesight was strained from trying to make out shapes in the mist; my ears were ringing from the effort to distinguish the distant sounds.

40 I was cut off from the world by the thick blanket of mist. My earlier lightheartedness had completely evaporated. I felt alone and confused.

I walked on along the path, which began to climb inland away from the sea. Ghostly shapes loomed up out

45 of the mist – they were sheep. Quite suddenly, the mist began to clear. Ahead of me rose the mighty shape of Calnwick Castle. Its ruined towers were surrounded by wisps of mist. A ghostly castle.

I looked at my watch and realized I'd spent over an

50 hour here. I decided not to spoil the illusion of the castle by going any closer, and set off back to the car. On my way back, I watched the slow movement of the sea. The remains of the mist hung over it like thin smoke.

55 By now it was four o'clock so I wasted no time in rejoining the road north to Edinburgh. A few miles along it, I turned off along a narrow road which wound along the bottom of the Scar valley. There were a few small villages with stone-built houses, huddling among clumps

60 of trees. As I went higher, the trees became scarcer and

14

more twisted, like crippled old men. I was soon in the high moorland, with its stone walls and windswept grass.

Suddenly, as I was rounding a sharp bend in the road at the bottom of a steep cliff-face, a boulder broke away and rolled down the slope towards the car. By sheer instinct, I accelerated. The boulder bounced once on the road just behind the car and crashed into some bushes below. I stopped the car by the side of the road and got out. I was shaking. It had been a very near miss. I walked back to the spot and looked down at the boulder. It lay nestled in some bushes. It was about the size of a human head. If it had hit the car, it would certainly have killed me.

I drove into the next village and parked. I needed something to calm my shattered nerves. There was only one street, with a small post office and a general store, a pub and a tea-room. I tried the tea-room. It was closed. It was too early for the pub to be open. I went into the general store. There were no other customers. The bell on the shop door jangled noisily but no one came to serve me. I waited a few moments, then called out, 'Anyone there?' There was no reply, only an eerie silence. I called again. Still there was no reply. I went back into the street. It was deserted. There was not a living soul in sight. I climbed back into my car and drove on.

As I drove out of the village, a football rolled out in front of the car, closely followed by a young boy. I screeched to a stop, my hands shaking on the wheel. The boy grabbed his ball and ran off down an alley between the houses. I sat for a few minutes trying to calm myself down. This journey was turning from a pleasant dream into a nightmare. The sooner I got to Clive's, the better! I drove on and soon turned off along a narrow track leading to the head of the valley.

Turning a corner, I suddenly saw Scarfell Place in

front of me. It was built of grey stone and fitted neatly into the landscape. It seemed to have grown there, rather than to have been built. Clive said that it had been built by one of the Dukes of Northumberland for his mistress, Margaret de Vere, back in the sixteenth century. It had been in Clive's family ever since, and had a long and violent history. According to Clive, it was haunted too. The ghost was Martin de Vere, Margaret's husband. The Duke had cut off his head, to make room for himself in the lady's bed.

I parked the car and went up to the front door. It was made of oak and studded with black iron nails. A note with my name was pinned on it.

Dear Sphinx (my nickname from our school days)

Sorry but I've had to pop out. I'll be back later. Make yourself at home. I've put you in the Valley Room (see plan below). The water's hot. Have a bath. There's cold chicken and salad and some wine in the fridge, and drinks in the cabinet, help yourself. The fire's laid – light it if it's chilly. Don't wait up for me. You must be whacked. See you tomorrow if not before.

Clive.

PS If you hear any noises in the night, don't worry – it'll be the plumbing; it's 400 years old!

I went in. It was just as I had imagined it; wooden panelling with old family portraits hanging in the gloom, and a great oak staircase leading to the first floor. I mounted the stairs, following Clive's plan. The house had been built in stages, with new bits added on every hundred years or so. As the corridor came to the end of each section of the house, there were a few steps to go down to the next section. The Valley Room was the last in the house and the corridor led straight to the door. When I opened the door I saw a large bay window

facing me. Through the window, I had a magnificent   130
view down the Scar valley, golden in the light of the May
evening. I felt my good spirits returning.

After a hot bath I went back down to the long lounge.
I helped myself to a large malt whisky, lit the fire (the
evening was chilly high up here in the hills) and stretched   135
out in one of the comfortable armchairs to read the
paper. I decided to wait for Clive. I hadn't seen him for
three years. I also realized that I had not spoken to
anyone all day. An evening chat would be welcome. I had
another whisky – lovely smoky flavour – and settled   140
down to wait. By eight-thirty Clive had still not returned,
so I ate the chicken and salad. There was an excellent
bottle of Bordeaux in the kitchen which went down well
with my meal. I made coffee and found some old Armag-
nac in the cabinet. The fire was burning low in the wide   145
old-fashioned fireplace; I put on more logs, then made
myself comfortable again. Several Armagnacs later I
found my head nodding. It was eleven – I must have
dozed off. I hastily cleared the table and went upstairs.

I could not find the light switch for the long corridor   150
so I had to feel my way by holding on to the wall. I was
feeling slightly dizzy. Forgetting about the steps leading
down from level to level, I missed my step on the first
ones, stumbling to my knees. Once back to my room, I
threw off my clothes and fell into the wide four-poster   155
bed. Sleep swallowed me up.

But it was not a quiet sleep. In my dreams bearded
heads grinned at me from the foaming blood where they
rolled. A stone head chased me along a winding road. I
could hear it rolling behind me; felt it coming closer . . .   160
A football rolled into the road in front of my car. It
turned into a child's head. Blood splattered all over my
windscreen . . . I woke up in a cold sweat, trembling. I
checked the time; three o'clock.

165   Then I heard it, the sound of something heavy rolling along the wooden floor of the corridor. I heard bump, bump, bump, as it rolled down the steps. It was some distance away. Was I still dreaming? But the rolling came closer, and went bump, bump, bump down the second set
170 of steps. I now heard another sound, the sound of footsteps, slow and farther away but coming nearer too. Now came the bump, bump, bump as the thing rolled down the last set of steps. It rolled towards my bedroom door with a rumble. I realized that, in my confusion, I had
175 forgotten to close my door. It rolled in and stopped under my bed. From the corridor came the sound of the approaching footsteps. Taking my courage in both hands, I took the pocket torch from the bedside table and shone it underneath the bed. The head looked at me with
180 imploring eyes and said, 'Ssssh! Keep it dark. Don't tell him I'm here.'

    The footsteps had almost reached my door. Suddenly they stopped. Then I heard them moving back along the corridor away from my room. I held my breath and
185 waited. After a few minutes I called under the bed, 'It's all right. He's gone now.' But there was no reply.

A Real Dark Horse

The wreath of chrysanthemums lay on the back seat, filling the car with their pungent aroma. We had collected it from the florist's shop early that frosty November morning. The white blooms were bruised grey with the cold.

Ma Tante Hortense's funeral was at eleven. We crossed the frontier into Belgium at nine. Soon we were approaching the town. The houses crouched under a low grey November sky. All around were the dark abandoned mine tips.

The big house stood in its own garden. There were black crêpe hangings around the door. The coffin stood on a table in the front room. Neighbours and friends came in and out, crossing themselves and dropping their visiting cards into a tray by the door. Michel, Hortense's only son, and his wife Ginette, stood by the door to shake hands and accept their sympathy. He was her closest surviving relative. He also secretly hoped to inherit most of her large fortune. He felt it was her duty to leave him the family fortune, after all the shame she had caused by living with Leopold.

I had not known Hortense well. What I did know about her came from family gossip. She was certainly a character! She had buried two husbands. Jean, the first, had been a rich landowner. (Michel had been the only

child of this marriage.) When Jean died, he had left her several farms and a tract of forest down south, near Beaumont. She had promptly married again, this time to Gustave, who was a broker on the Stock Exchange. He
30 had been killed in a hunting accident two years later, leaving her a fortune in shares and bonds, as well as the house in Brussels and this one in Charleroi.

She had not married again. Instead she had formed a relationship with Leopold. Leopold seemed an unlikely
35 lover for Hortense. She was a woman of the world; always expensively dressed, dripping with jewelry, eating in the best restaurants, always at the opera or the theatre. In short, she knew how to enjoy life. Leopold on the other hand had been an accountant in the steel-works
40 just outside town. He was 'ordinary'. He always wore the same kind of baggy, grey suit with heavy black lace-up shoes. His idea of fun was to watch TV games with a box of Belgian chocolates on his knee. Worst of all he was ten years younger than her.

45 Nobody knew how they had met. Nobody understood how they could possibly be attracted to each other. But apparently they were; they had lived in the same house together for nearly thirty years. He had gone on working at the steel-works until it closed when the company had
50 been taken over by a larger one in Germany. Since then he had spent most of his time at home, doing household chores and looking after the garden. Sometimes he did some accounting for people; preparing their tax returns. It seemed that he had a gift for money matters.

55 Above all, he had looked after Hortense. Hortense herself had gone on with her intense social life; she never took Leopold anywhere with her though. She also continued to manage her money and property, and spent a lot of time around the Stock Exchange.

60 In the family people unkindly said that Leopold was

just like a servant to Hortense; that she kept him because he was cheaper than a real servant. (But this could not have been quite true for in recent years she had employed a live-in Vietnamese maid, called Binh.) None the less, he had always been available to do whatever Hortense wanted for all those years. Who knows what their relationship was really like? Whatever it was, it had survived thirty years.

It was Leopold, assisted by Binh, who now served us coffee and brandy in the back parlour. Soon, after the usual confusion, the cortège formed up outside and we began our slow procession to the church. Luckily, it was not far off. I walked next to my grandfather, a distant cousin to Hortense. At eighty, he was bent almost double. I could see the top of his head, an unnatural white above his red peasant face. We had all removed our hats as a mark of respect.

'Damn these funerals. You have to walk everywhere. I wish I could put my cap on. Why couldn't she die in the summer? She always was an awkward bitch.'

When the service came to an end the coffin was wheeled out and lifted into the hearse for the long walk to the cemetery. It had begun to rain in icy arrows. As the procession trailed down the cobbled street the rain turned to sleet. The cobbles were slippery underfoot. Grandfather fell slowly behind until he was walking with Leopold at the back of the procession. 'If it's as far as this, I'm damned if I'm going to walk back! I'll call a taxi,' he grumbled.

We turned off the road into the cemetery. The sleet had now turned to snow. It took only a few minutes to slide the coffin into the vault alongside the two already there. The mourners pressed forward through the sticky mud to pay their last respects.

The group of family members made their way back to

21

the house. The crêpe hangings had already been removed
from the door. In the back parlour we were served hot
grog to warm ourselves. Soon about twenty of us were
seated round the big table ladling hot soup into our
100 plates. The meal was delicious and the wine flowed
freely. The religious atmosphere of the church was soon
replaced by the pagan enjoyment of food and drink, and
the telling of jokes and family stories. Through all of this
Leopold acted as a kind of butler, fetching and carrying
105 plates and re-filling empty glasses.

'Thanks Leopold,' said Michel, feeling his importance
growing by the minute, 'A little more of the Bordeaux I
think. Yes, and for Madame. Good.' Ginette, who kept
giggling at the wrong moment, tried to hold her glass like
110 a 'lady'.

The meal had been prepared by Binh, who flitted to
and fro carrying new dishes and taking away the dirty
plates. She was perhaps thirty years old, and very beautiful. Her natural elegance contrasted sharply with the
115 greedy behaviour of those she was serving. At one point
she had been removing a plate from Ginette, when
Michel, in a sweeping gesture had knocked it from her
hand. 'Shit! Can't you watch what you're doing?' he had
shouted.

120 She and Leopold seemed to work as a team. They
hardly ever spoke to each other but there was a sort of
silent understanding between them.

After the coffee and liqueurs the mood changed again –
to one of expectancy and anticipation. The *notaire* was
125 due at five to read Hortense's will. The table was cleared
and the family settled into their chairs to hear from the
lawyer what they had been left. I could feel the greed in
the air. The *notaire*, a grey man smelling of mothballs,
declined the offer of a liqueur and began reading the will
130 without delay.

'This is the last will and testament of Hortense, Louise, Philomène, Lambert, née Vanderhaas, dated this thirteenth day of September 1988. I leave all my property, <u>except as detailed below</u>, to my son, Michel.' Michel almost purred with pleasure. Ginette wriggled her plump 135 bottom on the velvet chair. The *notaire* continued, 'My house at 10, rue Baudouin, Charleroi, and its contents, I leave to Leopold van Teunen. The remainder of my assets consists of approximately 10,000 francs, in my account with the Banque des Pays Bas. There is nothing 140 else.'

Michel had gone pale, and sweat had broken out on his forehead. Ginette giggled. 'Shut up, you ninny,' he snarled. Addressing himself to the *notaire* he demanded, 'And what about the house in Brussels, and the estates 145 near Beaumont, and the shares, and all the rest? What the hell has happened to them?'

'I think, Monsieur, that Monsieur van Teunen could explain that better than I.'

Leopold stepped forward from the kitchen door, where 150 he had been standing with Binh. 'Your mother was not as good at business as you all imagined,' he said, a smile playing round his lips. 'Several times in the past twenty years she made bad investments, very bad. In the same period, I made some very good investments, small at 155 first, but progressively larger. Each time she was in trouble, she came to me for help. I helped her as much as I could. In exchange, she gradually transferred her property to me. It was also a way of avoiding the tax problem. So, all the property you mentioned now belongs to me, 160 I'm afraid.'

Michel had flushed red, then purple. I thought he would explode. 'You cheated her out of her property! You're a cheap confidence trickster, you jerk!'

'Monsieur, I beg you not to insult me. You neglected 165

your mother for years. When was the last time you visited her? All you could think of was the disgrace she had brought on you by living with me! You have no reason to accuse me. I helped your mother when nobody else would do so. I lived with her sarcastic comments. I put up with her bad temper. I waited up for her when she came back from her parties and dinners with all those snobbish people she would never let me meet. I took care of her when she was sick. I was like a servant to her, even though she treated me as if I was not there.

'And now I must ask you all to leave my house. Now! If you wish to purchase this house, for sentimental reasons, Maître Grandmal here has instructions to let you have it at a very reasonable price. Binh and I will be packing up shortly and moving to the Riviera. We intend to make the most of our life, just as she did. Goodbye everyone. I do not think we shall meet again.'

It was at this point that Grandfather, who had dozed off after too much wine, woke up. 'What's going on?' he asked. When I told him, his only comment was, 'Serve them right. But you were a real dark horse, Leopold. Good luck, my dear.' And he took advantage of the situation to plant a lingering kiss on Binh's cheek on the way out.

Man Proposes . . .

Bruce Nesbitt sipped his coffee appreciatively. Rosalind, his new secretary, certainly understood about coffee. It was just strong enough, without being bitter, and just sweet enough, without spoiling the taste of the special Arabica blend he always drank. Only the best was good 5 enough. And why not indeed? He certainly deserved it. He would be fifty tomorrow, and had worked his way up through the ranks of the company to become the youngest Chief Executive in its history. He had worked hard to get where he was. He had started as an office-boy and now 10 he was the big boss. Now he could look forward to another ten good years in control before 'retirement'. Then his reputation would bring him a string of company directorships and profitable consultancies as an 'elder statesman' of the business world. 15

Life was good and would get better. His wife was still an attractive woman and their son Alistair, just twenty-one, would be getting engaged to the daughter of Lord Bentwich this very evening. A grand party at Claridges Hotel had been arranged and . . . that reminded him. He 20 pressed the call button to call Rosalind; there was still the seating plan to finalize. Then there was the unpleasant bit of business with Jenkins to settle. Jenkins would have to go. He looked in the mirror and put on his 'important' face. Then he sat at his big desk and pretended to be 25 writing when Rosalind arrived.

Bill Jenkins looked at his haggard and unshaven face in the mirror of the staff toilets at the factory. He was the factory manager. He had stayed on until the early hours of the morning trying to get the figures to balance. But, whatever he did, the gap remained: an enormous hole down which, somehow, £50,000 had disappeared. He suspected that Alistair had taken it but he could not prove it. Anyway, it was more than his job as manager was worth to accuse the boss's own son of stealing it, with or without proof.

In the past three months he had been spending more and more nights like this at the factory. And more and more bottles of malt whisky had been keeping him company, helping to soften the blow which he knew would soon strike him.

Strangely enough, he now felt quite detached. His main worry was for Margaret and his daughter Mandy. What would become of them if anything happened to him? They had a very big mortgage – there was still £100,000 left to pay for the house. And there were all the specialists' bills for Mandy too. He sometimes wondered if she would ever be like other children.

His watch alarm suddenly started to ring, to remind him of the morning meeting. At least Alistair Nesbitt, with his nasty smile, would not be there; he was off somewhere in town running around with that rich bitch he was going to marry. Bill ran the electric razor over his chin and cheeks, combed his hair, straightened his tie and walked out bravely to face the day.

Margaret Jenkins sat on a bench in Hyde Park, keeping a watchful eye on Mandy. The child was chasing the pigeons in the dappled sunlight under the big plane trees.

It was spring and the lawns were splashed with clumps of bright yellow daffodils. She thought of her own childhood. There had been daffodils then too, but wild ones in the fields behind the farm. She often found herself remembering things like this these days. What if she had stayed on the farm and never gone to Cambridge, never met Bill, never had Mandy? . . .

She pushed these disturbing thoughts out of her mind as Mandy shambled towards her across the grass. In her hand the five-year-old child clutched a pigeon's feather. Mandy offered it to her like a precious possession. Her large head lolled to one side and her slack mouth dribbled saliva as always, but her eyes were bright with pleasure. Margaret took the feather and took her daughter into her arms. Some people walking by turned to look at them. In their eyes she recognized a mixture of pity and disgust. Never mind, she was used to it by now. How could they understand? Mandy slobbered and shrieked with delight.

Quite suddenly, Margaret felt terribly afraid – it was something to do with Bill. He had not been home again last night. But that did not worry her; he had stayed out many times before. In any case, he had phoned her several times from the factory last night. She felt that something very bad had happened to him. He was in some kind of trouble – she must get home at once and call him.

She tugged at Mandy's hand and half-led, half-dragged her towards the park gates. Their flat was only a few yards away across the busy highway; she would be home within a few minutes. They stood waiting for the traffic lights to change; there, green. It was safe to cross. Suddenly Mandy twisted out of her hand and ran across the road.

Alistair Nesbitt muttered to himself angrily as he inched

forward in the morning rush-hour traffic. The traffic was terrible. At this rate he would never be in time to pick Angela up at ten. And there was so much to be done before he met her father at the Club for lunch. He eased the Alfa Romeo into second gear and wove his way round a taxi, only to find himself behind a big delivery lorry. This stop-start log jam of vehicles seemed to go on as far ahead as he could see. It was made worse by the traffic lights at every intersection. They always seemed to be red.

Thank goodness he wouldn't have to go through this daily torture once he and Angela were married. His father had already promised him the manager's job at the factory. Today he would be getting rid of that twit Jenkins who ran it. Once Jenkins had gone, no one would ever find out about the money he, Alistair, had 'borrowed'. It would not be long. Then he'd be able to buy a house in the country, nearer Angela's parents and no farther away from the factory. And once they were married, there would be no more problems over money either. Lord Bentwich had already told his father, in confidence, that he would 'see the young couple off to a good start'. Lord Bentwich was a very wealthy man.

The traffic miraculously started to clear as he came up to the bottom end of Hyde Park. There was a good straight bit of road here. He would be able to make up some of the time he had lost. He changed into top gear and accelerated. He was in luck; a whole series of lights were green for him. He zoomed along, touching sixty miles an hour. The light ahead suddenly changed to orange. He thought that, if he accelerated, he would just get past it before it changed to red. He was only yards from it when it did change. Hell, what difference did it make anyway? He put his foot down. He hardly saw the small figure on the zebra crossing as it ran across in front of the car. All he felt was the sickening thump. The child's body lay like a heap of old clothes. In its hand it clutched a pigeon feather.   130

Bruce Nesbitt put down the receiver with a sigh of relief. He hated these unpleasant situations but it had been necessary to do it. In the event, it had proved easier than he had feared; Jenkins had seemed to be expecting it. Now there would only be the details to sort out: the size   135 of the compensation payment of lieu of notice, the actual date for Jenkins's departure, getting someone in to replace him for a few weeks till Alistair got back from his holiday with Angela. Personnel Department would take care of all that.   140

   The phone rang again. Rosalind explained that the police were on the line. They needed to speak to him urgently. It was probably about the break-in at the factory last month. He took the call. The expression of relaxed satisfaction faded from his face. As the call went on the   145 feeling of unease grew to a panic which filled his whole mind. He replaced the receiver. His face was grey as he left the office. There had to be a way of keeping this quiet – but how? And what about this evening's party? It was all so terribly inconvenient.   150

Paul

The place was easy enough to find again – the small turning to the right off the village street and the narrow entrance opposite the whitewashed church. He drove in and parked under the cypress tree. Yet it all seemed
5 strange. In his memory the village had been miles away from the town. Now it seemed almost part of it. But a child measures with its feet, and the distances of childhood are in the mind.

He shivered as he got out of the car. It had rained in
10 the night and there was still mist on the mountain. He had no idea if they still lived here. And at seven-thirty in the morning . . . He half hoped they had moved. Then he would be able to continue his journey with a clear conscience. The hallway was dark and dingy, just as he
15 remembered it. He peered at the tin mail boxes: Joxe, Montereau, Chanterel, . . . Portini – so the Portinis were still here! He mounted the three damp steps and rang the bell.

It took him a few seconds to recognize the tall figure
20 inside the door. Slowly the distinguishing features sharpened as his eyes became accustomed to the darkness: the paralysed right arm and the bullet scar on the right cheek. It was definitely Claude Portini.

'Yes? What can I do for you?'
25 'I'm, I'm sorry to disturb you so early but, but . . . I

was just passing through and I thought ... I am the English boy who stayed with you fifteen years ago.'

'David?'

'That's right.'

'What is it Claude? Who is it? What does he want?' There was a note of panic in the voice.

'It's all right Lily, wait there, I'll be back directly.'

'But who is it Claude?'

'It's all right Lily. It's David, you know, David, who stayed with us in . . .'

'David! No! I didn't recognize you. Come on in. Come in.'

Her voice was breathy, almost gasping. Her face was puffy and swollen. She had obviously just got out of bed. The few rooms they lived in now looked neglected. In the small hallway there were stacks of old newspapers. In the room which had been a dining-room, and where Paul had slept on a sofa during his stay, it was almost impossible to move. Yet this very room had once seemed the most spacious in the apartment, with its spotless, waxed Italian tiles.

He glanced quickly at the walls, searching for the framed case of medals. They had been the father's pride. They were his only reward for the paralysed arm and the scarred face. He had served in the Alpine Regiment. The walls were bare except for a copy of an old supermarket calendar.

There was an awkward silence.

'And are you still working for the railways?'

'Yes, yes. I retire next year. That will be over thirty years I've been with them. No one else has been with them as long. It's a record.'

He spoke drily with a trace of irony.

'I don't know what they're going to do without him. When he was off sick for a few days last year the Station

31

Master himself came round to visit, didn't he Claude? He said they needed him back as soon as possible. It's because he knows all the ins and outs, you see.'

She sounded childlike in her obvious admiration. The father showed no emotion. He had certainly heard it all before. What did they talk about, he wondered, if they talked at all?

He suddenly remembered the stories they had told about their courtship. How they had won the dancing competitions together. That had been before the war, before Claude's injury. Yet he still remembered the night they had gone to a fête in a nearby village, and how the parents had taken the floor like a ship in proud sail.

He offered a cigarette to the father.

'No thanks. I still roll my own.'

He took out his tobacco tin and cigarette papers and expertly rolled himself a thin cigarette.

'Monsieur David speaks very good French now, doesn't he, Claude?'

'That's because I'm married to a French girl.'

'Really? Where's she from?'

'The North.'

'Oh, the North. We don't know anyone from there, do we Claude?'

'No. In fact we don't know many people at all these days.'

The father smiled a sad smile as he spoke.

'And Paul? How is he? Is he married yet?'

'Paul is dead,' said the father.

'I'm . . . sorry. I didn't know. I . . . I'm sorry.'

'I thought you knew. I thought that we had written.'

'No. Forgive me. I had no idea. How did it happen?'

She looked on the point of tears – but none came.

'We don't really know do we Claude? He was engaged

to a girl from Chambéry. She was a Protestant. You're a Protestant aren't you?'

'Well, in a way, yes.'

'They were making trouble about the wedding – her people, I mean. Well we're not what you could call specially Catholic, but we didn't like that, did we Claude? She was a nice girl though. Really nice. But her parents wanted him to convert – to become a Protestant. They said they wouldn't let him marry her otherwise. He started to act very strangely. Sometimes he wouldn't talk to us for weeks. Then he'd stay here and refuse to see her again. I think he was suffering a lot. He wasn't the same person any more. He seemed to be torn in two. Well, he came home one weekend and we finally agreed to what they wanted. We couldn't bear to see him suffer like that any more, you see.

'Then, early on the Monday morning, we were called over to the café for an urgent telephone call from Albertville. It was the Director of the Teachers' College. They had found Paul dead in his room.'

The father broke in. 'We never found out exactly what happened. There were police investigations. It was all very upsetting, especially for Lily.'

'Then,' she continued, 'there was trouble with her parents about the burial. They said he'd even agreed to be buried as a Protestant. Can you believe it?! By then it was too late to argue. What could we do? He was dead anyway.'

Paul was dead. What did it mean to him? All he could really remember about Paul, apart from his dark, bird-like eyes, were the odd clothes he had been wearing when they had first met. The other memories of that summer were of himself rather than of Paul.

He could still remember their arrival at Chambéry from Paris. The train had crawled for hours through dry

hills. His throat was parched from the snacks of dry
saucisson, hunks of bread and harsh red wine. They had
walked from the station to the village in the afternoon
heat. In the village street they sat down at a metal table
135 outside the grocer's and were served a bright green liquid,
clinking with ice-cubes. It had tasted of perfection; he
had never again tasted anything quite like it.

Paul had taken him into the garden as soon as he had
unpacked. One of the new wonders was a plant which
140 oozed a bright orange dye when you broke its stem.

Everything had been new. He had never seen a mountain before; here he was surrounded by them. There
were no waterfalls in his flat homeland; here you could
find dozens within a few miles. And there were unknown
145 vegetables and strange new fruits and spiced cake and
wine and cherries preserved in alcohol, and . . .

And the smells! Coffee on a hot August morning as
you threw open the shutters. No one had shutters in
England!

150 During the month he had stayed they had become
close friends. They had cycled up the mountains and
zoomed back down again at breakneck speed. They had
gone together to the nearby lake where there were big
black catfish. They had swum in the milky blue water,
155 and lazed on the stones afterwards. They had hunted the
giant green lizards. But he had never broken through the
wall of strangeness around Paul.

'You'll have some coffee.'

'Thank you – but I've already had coffee at the hotel.'
160 'Never mind. I'll make a fresh pot.'

The aroma was not as he remembered it.

While she was in the kitchen the father lowered his
voice.

'He committed suicide. They found him hanging in his
165 room. We've never told Lily. She was too ill. In fact

she's never really recovered. I expect you noticed. She's still not exactly "well".'

'What are you two whispering about then? Me being ill? Well, yes, I was very ill. I don't remember much about it now. It's like a bad dream – you know it was bad but you can't remember the details. Then as I got better we preferred to stay at home. So we don't go out much.'

The father went on, 'After a bit we realized we couldn't spend the rest of our lives grieving over Paul. After all, life goes on, doesn't it?'

'But we still don't see many people, do we Claude? You can't go to people's houses and not eat; they get offended.'

'Anyway, I'll be retiring next year. Then we'll be moving into the block of flats they're putting up over there. I'm going to be the caretaker. At least it'll keep me occupied. Look, I'm sorry but I must be off, or I'll be late. Stay and talk to Lily. Better still, stay for lunch.'

'I'm sorry. I really can't. I have to get to the Spanish border by this evening.'

'That's a pity. You must come again though. Bring your wife next time. Just write and let us know. Goodbye David.'

He wheeled his bicycle out of the spare room and set off. This at least was as he remembered it. Cigarette glued to his lower lip, and steering the bike with his good arm, he pedalled off to his desk in the heart of the main railway station.

'Well, here's the coffee then.' She served him some of those spongy, sugar-covered biscuits that every French housewife seems to have stored away in a cupboard somewhere.

One afternoon they had walked to a village in the foothills. They went to buy apples for the winter. There had been Paul, himself, the mother and Signora Cortoni,

35

an old Italian immigrant. It was hot. They passed a ruined house.

'These people betrayed some resistance fighters so one night . . . boom.' The house had some shattered tiles
205 with the same pattern as the ones in their own dining-room. It was hot and the women perspired profusely and became bad-tempered. When they arrived at the farm-house there had been tepid drinks served in sticky glasses before they went in among the fruit trees to gather their
210 own fruit. The apples lay nestled like green eggs and smelt mellow and warm.

He tried but he could not recall a single instant of their journey home that day. Yet he could still remember the bright, bird-like eyes set in Paul's dark face.
215 And so it was. Paul was dead. He made his excuses to the mother and left. She saw him to the door. Paul was dead and he was alive, though filled with the sense of his own mortality. On his way back to the car, he walked over to the garden wall and broke off the stem of a small
220 green plant. The bright, orange juice with the familiar, bitter smell stained his finger ends.

Cold Comfort

Ken woke from a confused dream. Gradually his eyes focussed. The first thing he noticed was a hand a few inches in front of his face. The fingers were like a bird's claw, stiff, blue with cold. With a shock, he realized that the hand belonged to him. At the same time, he became 5
fully aware of just how cold he was. His bones felt like frozen lead. He remembered an incident from the previous day; he had been hanging about near the kitchen entrance of the Strand Palace Hotel, scavenging for scraps, when a delivery van arrived. The driver had 10
carried in whole sides of beef, the red and white meat refrigerated into hard blocks. He now felt like that frozen meat, his back was as cold and stiff as a corpse.

He shifted gingerly and pulled the old army overcoat tighter round him for warmth. Suddenly he noticed it. 15
At first he thought it must be part of a dream. It was a ten-pound note! It was wedged between two of the sheets of cardboard in the doorway he shared with Tam and Nicko. They were both sleeping heavily. He saw two empty litre bottles lying between them and knew that 20
they would not wake easily. He snaked out his hand, grabbed the note, and rolled it into a tight ball in his palm. Though he was cold, he realized that he was also sweating with excitement, and with fear that they might wake up. 25

Slowly and silently, so as not to rouse the other two, he got up, gathered up his old bag and folded the cardboard away. Then he made his way furtively up Holborn Kingsway towards the tube station. In a side-street he squatted
30 in a doorway and carefully smoothed out the crumpled note. It didn't look like a fake. It was a real ten-pound note! He had no idea how it had got into the crack between the sheets of cardboard. Perhaps a late-night drunk had dropped it. Perhaps a wealthy theatre-goer
35 had taken pity on them as they slept. Never mind how it had got there. The main thing was that it had, and that it was now in *his* hand and not in someone else's.

It reminded him of the morning, six months before, when he had arrived in London from the north. By then
40 he'd been out of work for nearly two years after leaving school, and the prospects of finding a job were getting worse, not better. His dad had just lost his job too. The atmosphere at home had become so thick with anger and bitterness that he'd decided he'd be better off on his
45 own. If only he had known! He'd arrived in London with just £20 in his pocket; two of those brown and orange pieces of paper, just like the one he had just found. Within a week they were spent. Since then he had lived from hand to mouth, begging, borrowing, occasion-
50 ally stealing and, even less often, finding temporary, daily paid work on building-sites, in restaurant kitchens ... It was a long time since he had owned a ten-pound note.

He sat for a few minutes, trying to decide what to do
55 with this golden discovery. It would not be enough to buy him a bus ticket back to Newcastle, let alone a rail fare. And·anyway, he could not go back now. It was too late for that. He could spend it all on a really good meal; God knows, he needed one – he hadn't eaten properly in
60 months. But then it would be gone, and he would be no

better off than before. It had to be something that would make his money *grow*. But what?

It wasn't enough to invest on the Stock Exchange! He needed something that would bring him a quick return. He suddenly felt that this was his lucky day. It was a day when anything he touched would turn to gold. The more he thought about it, the more convinced he became that it was true. He made up his mind, walked quickly to the newspaper stand outside the tube station and exchanged his note for coins.

It was still only nine in the morning. The office workers were beginning to pour out of the station to begin their dreary day in banks, insurance offices and investment companies. They looked like puppets controlled by invisible strings. For a moment, he felt superior; he had chosen to be 'free'. But then he realized that being free was no use if you didn't have the money to enjoy it. He wandered off towards Covent Garden and sat down in a smoky espresso coffee bar to wait for the amusement arcades to open at ten.

At ten o'clock he was waiting impatiently for the place in Tottenham Court Road to open. It was ten past ten before the scruffy-looking attendant opened the doors to the public. Ken looked at his own reflection in the long mirrors by the entrance. He saw a dirty and unshaven youth with long unwashed hair, dressed in filthy jeans and a threadbare army overcoat. He rushed inside, went to the first machine, inserted a coin and pulled down the handle. There was the tinkling sound of cascading coins. He had hit the jackpot – first time round. He counted out his winnings: £15.30. He moved to the next machine.

By the time he left the arcade at twelve-thirty, he had won the unbelievable sum of £175.20. He wanted to continue but the manager, a thick-set, dark man with a scar down one cheek, warned him to leave in case 'an

accident' happened. He went into the first bank he came
to and changed his winnings into notes. It was then that
he noticed them. The man was about his own age, but
smartly dressed with designer shoes and an expensive-
looking Italian-style overcoat. The girl looked younger.
She had waist-length black hair, tight-fitting jeans and a
thick cashmere sweater. She was very beautiful.

He had seen them hanging about just inside the entrance to the arcade. Now they were in the bank. He
thought they might be following him. To test his theory,
he walked out of the bank and went into the nearest
eating place, which was a Greek taverna. He saw down at
a table in a corner away from the window. As he ordered
'moussaka' (it was the only thing on the grease-stained
menu he'd ever heard of), the couple entered the restaurant and sat down at the next table. He began to panic. He
could feel the thick wad of banknotes in his pocket. He
wondered if they could see it. But he need not have
worried. They did not try to mug him on the way out or
to get the money from him in any other way. All they did
was to start a conversation with him. By the end of the
meal, they were like old friends.

They left together and went to a nearby pub. Here
they fell into conversation with Charlie. Charlie told him
that he knew all about horse racing. He had spent his life
among the horses, the trainers and the jockeys. He told
Ken that he had inside information about the horses
racing at Epsom that very afternoon. He knew which
horse would win. For the price of a drink ('double
brandy, thanks') Charlie said he would give Ken this
information. Now Ken *knew* that this was his lucky day.
He felt it in his bones. Nothing he did could go wrong. A
horse winning a race at 100 to 1 – that would be real
money. After another round of drinks, which he heard
himself ordering – and paying for – they all went round

the corner to the betting shop. He decided to put all but £20 on Luxor to win in the 3.30. He was a bit worried to find that only £150 remained of the £175 he had won earlier – but he would work out where the rest had gone later. Anyway, from now on he would never need to worry about money again. One hundred and thirty pounds at 100 to 1, that would be £13,000! His calculations were interrupted by the others. They wanted to return to the pub. The pub had a TV and the race was going to be televised live.

Another round of drinks later, the race began. He felt a combination of fear and excitement in the pit of his stomach as the horses left the starting post and galloped into the first bend. He drained his glass and ordered another. At the half-way mark, Luxor was lying well back behind ten other horses. They all started shouting encouragement, 'Come on Luxor! You can do it, Go, Luxor, go!' Miraculously, a few hundred yards from the finishing post, Luxor began to pass the other horses. It finished a whole length ahead of the second horse. Luxor was the winner! He had won! His head was spinning with excitement and with the whisky he had drunk. He turned to the others – but they were gone! He looked for them in the other bar but they were not there either. The barman told him they had slipped out at the very end of the race. He couldn't understand it. They should all be celebrating together. Why had they gone? He felt in his pocket for the betting slip. Then he remembered that the girl had taken it 'to keep it safe and bring you luck'. A wave of sickness swept over him; he felt the world spinning out of control. Then the wave swallowed him in darkness. He had fainted.

Ken woke from a confused dream. Gradually his eyes focussed. The first thing he noticed was a hand a few inches in front of his face. The fingers were like a bird's claw, stiff, blue with cold. With a shock, he realized that the hand belonged to him. At the same time, he became fully aware of just how cold he was ... Suddenly he noticed it. It was a ten-pound note.

Alfred's Enigmatic Smile

'How about another cup of tea?' asked Alfred, with a
faint smile. I looked at my half-drunk cup and shook my
head.

'I don't blame you,' he said, 'It's not like your mum's
is it, my old stick-in-the-mud?'   5

'Stick-in-the-mud' – one of the many nicknames he
had called me by when I was a kid, back in the village. It
brought back all the flavour of that time, just after the
war, when his family and mine had lived next door to
each other.   10

In fact, his only family by then had been his wife
Sarah. They had had two sons. One of them had died of
polio aged nine. His picture, tinted and misty, had hung,
like an angel's, above the piano. The elder son had married
early – too early for comfort; they'd had a baby six   15
months later – and Sarah never spoke to her son again.

They had called him in from the prison garden as soon as
I arrived. Now he sat facing me across the stained wooden
table in that drab visitors' room with its faded cushion
covers and its out-of-date magazines. He looked almost   20
as I remembered him, which surprised me, after everything that had happened. He wore a long navy-blue
gardener's apron, just like the one he had worn as gardener at the Grange.

43

25 His hands, resting lightly clasped on the table, were as powerful as ever. They made me shiver as I remembered what I had seen them do. Once they had picked up five small kittens. I had watched him put them in a sack, then calmly drop the sack into a tank of water. Those hands
30 had held the sack under water until the bubbles stopped. He had smiled his strange smile and said, 'Sometimes you have to be cruel to be kind.' But he looked as if he had enjoyed it.

I remembered thinking that I had never seen Alfred
35 laugh. I had never seen him angry either. And never heard him raise his voice. In fact he never really showed his feelings. He smiled. But it was a pitiless smile. His smile was a mask. I had not realized what lay behind it.

It was true that he had little to smile about. His life
40 was a monotonous routine, interrupted by repeated bad luck. Apart from losing both his sons, each in different ways, he was married to Sarah. She was a large woman, in her fifties at that time. She had a large flabby body, protruding eyes and thinning grey hair through which
45 her scalp was plainly visible. Her skin was waxy, the colour of putty. She had a very loud, penetrating voice. She used it in her many arguments with her neighbours, but mostly she used it on Alfred. She was a diabetic. Alfred had to give her her daily injections of insulin.
50 'You're hurting me, you ape,' she would shout. We could hear her from next door. 'Be careful, damn you! Look at the bruises.' We all thought she was terrible to him. But he always smiled that smile. The same smile as when he had drowned the kittens. Later I wondered if he had hurt
55 her on purpose after all.

Alfred worked as the gardener at the Grange, the biggest, grandest house in the village. Its owner, Cedric Grimes, made his money from the business of undertaking. After all, there's nothing more certain than death.

44

Everyone has to die. And someone gets paid to bury them. Apart from tending the large gardens, Alfred had to help carry the coffins when needed. On those occasions he would be transformed – wearing his pin-striped trousers, black tail-coat and carrying his black silk top-hat in his hand. 'Alfred's gone on a job,' Sarah would explain. She never used the word 'funeral' itself.

Otherwise, Alfred's days were as predictable as the BBC. At ten to eight every morning from Monday to Saturday he would leave the house and walk the two hundred yards to the Grange. There he would work in the gardens until twenty-five past twelve. Then he would carefully take off his blue apron, hang it behind the shed door and make his way home for lunch. At twenty past one he trudged back to work, except on Saturdays which were a half-day, coming back at five sharp, to prepare Sarah's tea. We would often speak to each other as he passed our gate.

'Hello, Mr Philps. How are you?'

'Mustn't grumble,' was the inevitable reply. 'What have you been up to at school then, you ragamuffin?'

'Oh, trigonometry, and French and . . .'

'Jack of all trades, master of none, eh?' And he would walk on.

I remembered how he had often spoken in proverbs. Perhaps these ready-made phrases were a part of the mask he hid behind, like the smile itself.

The tea was now cold. I tried to draw him into conversation.

'How are things here now?'

'Oh, I mustn't grumble you know. I'm used to it now. Better the devil you know . . . I was sorry to hear about your dad.'

'Yes. Anyway, Mum seems to be getting over it.'

'Mm. Time is a great healer,' he said, meaningfully,
95   and smiled.

'So you do some gardening then?'

'Oh, yes. They put me in charge of the garden. I spend most of the time out there. I'll show you my chrysanthemums later, if you're not in a hurry.'

100   'So you still grow chrysanthemums then?'

'Oh, yes. You can't teach an old dog new tricks you know,' he said, and he smiled his cold smile again.

Alfred had in fact been a wonderful gardener, a man with 'green fingers'. His hobby was growing chrysanthe-
105   mums, and the whole of his garden was filled with them. He would spend hours nipping out the top leaves with those cruel fingers. In autumn they would unfold their hard buds into plate-sized blooms of bronze and white and pink and yellow, each one a mass of petals as tightly
110   curled as watch springs. Then he would sell them to the local florist for a good price. He would never bargain. 'You get what you pay for; take it or leave it,' he would say.

At the time I recall most clearly, Sarah had become a
115   total invalid. She had gone into a coma once, after eating too much sugar. A few weeks later, she had a mild stroke, which left her speech slurred and the side of her face paralysed. Not long after that, she had some of her toes amputated; she had developed gangrene. She spent her
120   time in bed, gossiping with neighbours who called to see her. My own mother spent a lot of time with her, especially while Alfred was at work.

Her illnesses had not improved her temper. She would frequently burst into fits of rage for the least thing. Alfred
125   continued to weather these storms. When she shouted at him, he smiled. I once heard her say to him, 'What good are you to anyone? You let Norman die. You let Jack

marry that bitch. You can't even stop what's happening to me.' I had overheard their conversation as I came up the steps to their back door. 'Hello, my old fellow-my-lad,' Alfred had said, 'Don't worry about Sarah. Every cloud has a silver lining, you know.'

'I don't know how he puts up with it. If it was me, I'd strangle her!' my father used to say. 'Don't you say that,' my mother would reply, 'You should be ashamed of yourself.' But I couldn't help wondering if Alfred ever shared my father's thoughts. What went on behind Alfred's enigmatic smile? What feelings did it hide?

It was about this time that my mother arranged for me to go to their house every afternoon to practise on the Philps's piano. We did not have one of our own. Perhaps she wanted to have someone in the Philps's house in case anything happened to Sarah. So every afternoon from four to five I would bang away at my scales and the silly pieces set for me by my teacher Miss Croop. I still remember the cheerless living-room with its bare linoleum and the photograph of Norman. The piano echoed in the empty room. I would usually leave just before Alfred returned and would put my head round the bedroom door to say goodbye to Sarah. Usually she was in a semi-coma. When she wasn't, she would bellow, 'Make sure you shut the door properly behind you.' I always felt relieved when I had left that house.

On that last occasion, I was about to go in when I saw that the door was ajar. Through the opening I could see Sarah sitting on the side of the bed. She was half-naked and her great flabby body shook with her sobs. 'I can't stand it any more,' she moaned. 'You're useless, Alfred. Why can't you do anything? I can't bear the pain . . . Do something to help me, damn you.' Alfred had his back to me. 'You want me to do something, do you, you fat bitch?' he said quietly. 'All right then, I'll do something.'

I watched his strong hands pick up the hypodermic syringe and draw some liquid into it. Then he grabbed her arm roughly and sank the needle deep into it. She screamed once, then fell back on to the bed. I tip-toed away and let myself out quietly through the back door.

The funeral took place a week later. It was autumn, and Alfred's chrysanthemums were in full bloom. On the night before the funeral he took out his powerful secateurs. Very deliberately he cut every one of them to fill the funeral hearse the next day. It was like a massacre. I watched him from behind the curtains: he was smiling.

Alfred returned to work the following Monday. 'The devil makes work for idle hands,' he remarked with a cheerless smile. To begin with no one suspected anything. After all, Sarah had sunk into a coma before. Only this time she had not come out of it. What could be more normal? But then there was the coroner's report. He had ordered an autopsy. Only I knew why. That was the end of Alfred.

It was Friday when the police arrived to take him away. 'It's an ill wind that blows nobody any good,' he said, as they pushed him into the police-car. What happened at the trial is still a blur for me, but the words 'while the balance of his mind was disturbed' still ring in my ears.

As we walked down into the garden, I asked, 'Why did you do it?' We were now among the chrysanthemums. Some of them were beginning to open. Alfred took a pair of sharp gardener's secateurs from his apron pocket. I heard the stalks crunch as he severed six blooms. He handed them to me and said, 'The survival of the fittest. Now let me ask you a question. Who tipped off the coroner?'

Then he smiled his enigmatic smile.

Esivi

'I'm afraid I owe you an explanation. It's a long story. And you may find it difficult to believe.'

My colleague Dr Hanson had rooms facing mine at the top of E staircase in Chapel Court at St Jude's College. We knew each other quite well. We'd lived opposite each other for ten years now and often invited each other for morning coffee or a glass of sherry before dinner at High Table. He was a bachelor, like me. He used to say that he was married to his work. He was a senior lecturer in the Psychology Department. What he had learned about the human mind was enough to stop him from marrying (or so he said). My own reasons for not marrying were different. But I shall come to that later. Anyway, Hanson had never seen a woman in my rooms in all the ten years we had known each other. The previous night, he had opened his door at 3 a.m. (he suffered from insomnia) to find a slim, attractive twenty-year-old kissing me fondly goodnight. He had told me at breakfast that he was 'extremely shocked'. Particularly as the young lady was black. So I had invited him over for coffee later the same morning, to explain what had happened.

'Did you know that I worked in Ngara for several years? It was my first job. I was a junior lecturer in a College of Education about fifty miles from the capital, Akawa. Binewa was the name of the place – just a small

fishing town on the coast. There was one main street, full
of dust and garbage being picked over by mangy dogs. It
was lined with corrugated-iron roofed shops all selling
the same assortment of cloth, kerosene, groundnuts, palm
oil, matches, cigarettes and various kinds of hoes and
cutlasses. There were a few dressmakers' shacks – "Comfort's Clothes", "Charity Ntsiful Dressis Pass All" – you
know the kind of thing if you've ever been to West
Africa. The people there scratched a living from a mixture
of petty trading, subsistence farming and fishing.

'The College had been built by the colonial administra-
tion as part of the preparations for independence. There
were about five hundred students, who lived in dormi-
tories. Most of the staff lived in quite comfortable bunga-
lows. Mine was in a secluded corner of the compound
with papaya trees at the back and a large mango in
front. The teaching was not very demanding but the
students were a joy – so full of life and energy, and
optimism for the future. The country had not been independent long. It had an air of vibrancy. Some people
were already complaining about the politicians but they
were a minority, or so I thought. Esivi soon proved me
wrong.

'Life was simple; there was not that much to do in
Binewa. There was a run-down club near the beach
where we sometimes went for a game of tennis – until
termites ate the wooden net posts. You could go there for
a few bottles of Star beer in the evening, or even for a
game of snooker on the moth-eaten billiard table. But
that was about all. We would sit around for a few hours
in the creaking cane chairs, exchanging jokes and college
gossip, then stroll back to bed. I remember I always slept
so well there. We only had fans; there was no air-condi-
tioning then. Anyway we didn't need it as there was
always a sea-breeze at night. What I remember most is

the sound of the surf, pounding steadily throughout the night. Better than a sleeping pill!

'About once a month I would drive into Akawa and spend the weekend. I usually went dancing at the Akasimba Hotel. I've never forgotten the atmosphere of those Saturday nights, dancing the highlife in the middle of a swaying throng of people enjoying themselves in such a wholehearted way. There was the music, the rhythm, the dance – and the dancers totally absorbed in the dance. I wonder if I'd be any good at the highlife now?'

Hanson coughed a little uncomfortably. I do not think he had ever danced even to the waltz, let alone to the exotic rhythms of the highlife.

'One week I helped run a teachers' course in the capital. It was there that I met Esivi. Our eyes met during my first lecture. From then on we couldn't take our eyes off each other. She was tall with very fine features and a skin the colour of milk chocolate. And when she laughed, her whole face exploded with joy. There was no chance to meet her during the course but at the farewell tea party, after the ritual of the group photograph, she came up to me. "Now I have come to know you, when will I see you again?" This may seem rather direct to you but that is what happened. I told her it would be difficult for me to come to Akawa again for some time. "Then I will come to you," she said, "Next Sunday I will come. I will prepare food for you. Is it fine?"

'She came as promised. She had taken a Mammy-truck from Akawa early in the morning. The moment she stepped through the door, the place was transformed, by her laughter, by the way she moved, by the magic she brought to everything she did. After coffee we went to buy fresh fish and vegetables – okra, tomatoes, peppers –

and "leaves" in which to steam the fish. She took over
the kitchen and set to work. It was mid-afternoon before
we ate but the food was so delicious it was worth the
wait. As we ate, we talked.

100 'I have never felt so totally at home with anyone. It
was as if we had always known each other. She told me
that she came from the Eastern Province. She worked in
a primary school, sending most of her salary home to her
mother. Her father had died in prison fighting for inde-
105 pendence. Her mother had struggled to give her an education. As we talked, it became clear that she had very
strong political opinions.

'"You don't realize. You are a foreigner. You think
that independence has brought freedom! That's a joke.
110 Before we had white men ruling us. That was bad but
not as bad as the black white-men we have now. They
grab everything for themselves. If you get in their way,
bad things happen to you, especially if you are an Agbe
like me. They killed my brother last year. They called it
115 an accident. But they won't rule for ever. We are getting
organized at last."

'She was quivering with anger and emotion. I took her
hand.

'"David, the army will soon take over. Any day now
120 there will be a *coup d'état*. That's why I came to see you
now. Afterwards it may be too late. The army will put
some of them in jail and shoot the rest. But the army will
be even worse. They won't bring freedom either. When
the *coup* comes I will have to disappear. It will be too
125 dangerous for me. I'm on their list of wanted persons.
All the People's Freedom Party people will have to go
into hiding. We have to organize the struggle."

'I began to ask her a question but she put her lips
gently to my mouth and kissed me.

130 '"David, I came because I love you and because I

52

know I have to leave you. It will be easier for me to disappear from here than from Akawa. They were already watching me there. Please don't ask me anything else. We mustn't waste the little time we have together."

'Time had passed so quickly that it was already dusk. 135 We both knew that she would not be returning to the capital that night. She stayed with me for three days and three nights. Nothing that has happened in my life has ever been so important. I have never loved anyone again.

'On the fourth morning I woke early. I stretched out 140 my hand. There was no one there. The pillow was cold. I jumped up and searched the bungalow. Esivi and all her things had gone. On the table there was a note.

Darling David,

My comrades came for me. The *coup* will take place tonight. 145 I have to hide.

David – I can't tell you how hard it is for me to leave you. But I must. I will love you always. Never forget that. Perhaps one day, when this is all over, I will find you again.

Goodbye my love, 150

Esivi.

'I was stunned. I made a cup of coffee. My hands were shaking. I turned on the radio. ". . . is General Okugwo speaking on behalf of the National Liberation Council. This morning at five-thirty the valiant freedom-loving 155 soldiers of the National Army overthrew the tyrannical rule of the despotic dictator Kwesi Owusu. The National Liberation Council is dedicated to the restoration of freedom and the rule of law. The corrupt Owusu regime is no more. Please remain calm and stay at home until 160 further announcements are made. Long live Ngara!" The national anthem came on, followed by military music. So it was true. I thought about what Esivi had told me – that the army would be worse. I trembled to think of the danger she was in. 165

'In the next few weeks the army rounded up the supporters of the old regime. Some were put in jail, others were shot. The generals then began to arrest "dissidents"; most of them were people who had opposed the old regime. They "disappeared". Occasionally corpses were washed up on the beaches near the capital. It was a reign of terror. No one was safe. And I had no way of reaching Esivi.

'Two weeks later all foreign nationals were expelled from the country. I had an hour to pack and leave on the army lorry. It took me straight to the airport. I just had time to leave a note with my friend Kwesi Tamako. I gave him my address in the UK and asked him to pass it on to anyone who needed it. Twenty-four hours later I was in my flat in London. Outside a cold rain was falling.

'I have never been back to Ngara. Since I left there has been one *coup* after another but freedom has still not arrived. Many Ngarans have visited me – passed on by Kwesi. But none of them had news of Esivi. As you know, I have never married. Now you know why. I still have the note she left. And every morning of my life I hear in my mind the pounding of the surf, and stretch out my hand, hoping to feel her lying next to me.

'I now know that will never be. They shot her last year. I hope you will forgive the disturbance last night. But it isn't every day that one meets one's twenty-year-old daughter for the very first time.'

The Man Who Talked to Trees

They were twins; boys born five minutes apart in the dark days of the Civil War fifty years earlier. The elder was named Torbash, which means 'hero' in our language. The younger one's name was Milmaq, 'bringer of mercy'. Torbash had struggled like a hero to escape from his mother's womb, almost tearing her apart. Milmaq had slid out with merciful swiftness.

They were identical twins. When they were children strangers could not tell them apart. They both had dark black hair and piercing green eyes. They were strong, tall and erect. Until they reached their early teens, they were always together. They slept together, ate together, played together, went to school together, got into trouble together – they even fell ill together. And they looked after each other. Anyone who tried to bully one of them would face the anger of the other. And of course they used their physical likeness to play tricks on people, especially at school.

By the time they were fourteen the family had returned to its lands in the Nirmat valley. Their father had rebuilt the old farmhouse, destroyed by the retreating rebel army at the end of the war. He farmed the bottom of the valley, growing wheat and tending the rich almond orchards for which the valley was then famous. On the lower slopes he had vineyards from which he produced

55

the strong Nirmat Kashin (Lion of Nirmat) wine. The higher land was forested. The chestnut trees gave nuts in the autumn. The oaks and beeches, as well as the chestnut trees, were carefully tended. Their valuable timber was sold to furniture makers and builders in Jalseen, the town lower down the valley. The trees were cut according to a strict rotation. For every tree they cut down, another was planted. These were what we, the ones who remember, still call 'The Days of Contentment'.

It was about this time that the two boys began to grow apart. There was nothing sudden about this. They did not argue about a girl, or fight over an imagined insult as so many young people do. It was simply that they gradually began to do things by themselves which, before that, they would have done together. So each began to develop different interests.

Torbash spent his spare time hunting in the forests. He had been given a shotgun for his fifteenth birthday. He would proudly return after a day's hunting with wild pigeons, with rabbits, their eyes glazed in death, and sometimes with a deer. His greatest ambition was to bring back a wild boar. His other main occupation was to visit Jalseen, where there were girls with 'modern' ways. It was there that he got to know the 'contacts' who were to help him later.

Milmaq was a solitary person. He would spend hours in the forest, not hunting, simply sitting still, watching, waiting for something to happen. A spider would swing its thread across the canyon between two branches. A woodpecker would drum at the trunk of a chestnut tree, its neck a blur of speed. Above all, the trees themselves would speak to him. He would be aware of them creaking and swaying in the wind. He could sense the sap rising in them in the springtime; feel their sorrow at the approach of winter. If he put his ear to the trunk of a tree, he could hear it growing, very slowly; feel it moving towards its final magnificent shape.

Sometimes he would speak aloud to a tree. More often he would communicate with it silently. Sometimes he would lose all sense of himself. It was as if he had become part of the tree. This may sound like nonsense to you. Things are different now. But we still have an expression for this in the old language: '*Ahashinat ain kashul*'. It means, 'Finding the centre'.

Please do not think that the brothers lost touch with each other, in that special way that twins have. There was the time, one winter's evening, when Milmaq suddenly got up from the table, pulling his father with him, and set off for the upper slopes of the valley. Snow had fallen, and they soon found the tracks of boots and, soon after that, boar tracks. They found Torbash crouching in the branches of an oak tree. Beneath the tree there was a full-grown wild boar, grunting angrily.

It had a wound in its side. Their father killed it with the two barrels of his own hunting gun. And no one, least of all Torbash, ever asked how Milmaq had known he was in danger.

Just as Milmaq himself did not ask when Torbash arrived, as if by magic, to fight off the gang of thugs who had attacked Milmaq in the street on one of his rare visits to Jalseen. They were twins – '*majeen taq asnaan*' ('a plum with a double stone'). It was natural. No one thought it in the least bit strange.

It was not long after the incident with the boar that their father died. It was the time of the grape harvest. He had gone out after supper to check on the fermentation of the grapes in the vat. They found him floating in the vat, face downwards. He must either have had a heart attack or been overcome with the powerful fumes. Whichever, he was well and truly dead, and there was nothing anyone could do about it. As we say, '*Fashan kat maan nat, maan q'a nat*.' ('When the time comes, the time has come.') He was a brave man, respected by all, and regretted by all.

He and his wife had survived many hardships together. But she could not bear to live alone. Within three months, she had followed her husband to the place where all sufferings cease. The two boys were left alone.

It was not long before Torbash left home. He had never enjoyed the hard work of the farm. He needed to see things happen fast. He took a room in Jalseen and was soon working in one of the newer places there. It was a sort of restaurant, but nothing like anything we had seen before. It sold flat cakes of minced beef mixed with sawdust (or that's what it tasted like to us), grilled and served between two pieces of bread. The prices were high but young people loved it. Torbash began by washing up the dirty dishes. Within weeks he was 'supervising'. Soon afterwards, one of his 'contacts' offered him a better job with a company selling a new type of drink. It was brown and had a sweet, perfumed taste. And instead of quenching your thirst, it made you want to drink more. Give me a bottle of Nirmat Kashin any day! The drink was made in a factory in the capital and, before long, Torbash was promoted and went to work there in the head office. We did not see him for several years.

Meantime Milmaq continued to farm the family land. He did not marry, and seldom left the farm. When he was not on the land he would be in the woods. There were rumours that he was becoming more and more strange. Hunters had found him deep in conversation with an oak tree. He would walk through the woods greeting individual trees like old friends. And he completely stopped the cutting of timber for sale. The only trees he cut were dead or diseased. After several years, he closed up the old farmhouse and moved to an old forester's hut up on the edge of the woods. He only took a few essential belongings with him – a bed, a table, a chair, an old cooking stove and such like. Here he was closer to his beloved trees. He had become a sort of hermit, what we used to call '*Horat vanah*' (holy man). We respected him and left him alone, though occasionally one of us would pass by just to ask if he needed anything.

One day Torbash arrived unexpectedly. He was dressed in one of those modern suits, a shirt with red stripes and a bright red tie to match. He was driving a big red car which made a lot of dust when it roared into the village. He told us he was now a big man in another company. What sort of company? It made 'paper products', things like toilet paper and paper handkerchiefs. (We didn't know what these were but we didn't show it.) They also made paper for printing books and newspapers. And a special part of the company made furniture.

He had come to see his brother about selling the woods. We directed him to the forester's hut. He left his car and went on foot up the steep path. Now I should explain that, under our laws of inheritance, everything is left to the eldest son, '*Zirmat akal*' (first born). So the farm and the woods belonged to Torbash, even though it was Milmaq who worked them.

I don't know what happened when they met but, when Torbash came back down, his face was black with anger. He drove off without greeting us. A week later great machines began to arrive, ploughing up the tracks as they went up the hillsides. The trees began to be torn savagely, not in the old way. On the hillside away from the forester's hut there were soon no trees left, only a tangle of fallen trunks and smashed branches waiting to be sawn up and dragged away.

When I called to see Milmaq I found him in his bed. He was terribly thin and had a high fever. I kept watch

over him for the next three days. During this time, the
machines were moving closer and closer to the hut. Soon
there were only a few trees still standing. Until, through
the window, I could see just one tree left. It was a
170   magnificent oak, the one which Milmaq had often spoken
to. The men moved in with their evil-sounding saws and
began work. I watched, hypnotized by the enormity of
this massacre of trees. Behind me I heard Milmaq stir.
He staggered to his feet and leaned on the window sill.
175   The oak shuddered, swayed and, with a gut-wrenching
groan, crashed in a pile of splintered branches. As it hit
the ground, Milmaq himself collapsed. He was dead. I
looked at the clock. It was three in the afternoon. In the
distance I heard the rumble of thunder from the next
180   valley.

     We only heard about Torbash later. He had apparently
left a meeting in his office and driven off at high speed.
All he had said was, 'My brother. My brother.' In his
desperate haste, he had taken a short cut along a forest
185   track leading from the next valley to our own. A violent
thunderstorm had blown up – the one I had heard from
Milmaq's hut. An enormous oak tree had been struck by
lightning. It had fallen across the track, crushing the car
and Torbash with it. The crash had stopped the car
190   clock. Its hands pointed to three.

     I have finished. My story is told. *'Fashan kat maan
nat, maan q'a nat.'*

Miracles Do Happen

'Billings, Cooper and Parks. How can I help you?'

It was 5 p.m. on a Friday and Tracy was just about to leave.

'Yes. Could I please speak to Mr Michael Johnson? It is a personal call. But it is, ja, very urgent.'

Tracy was in a hurry to get away. She had a date with Vince at 5.30. Why did they always call at closing time on a Friday? But the man sounded upset, and he was obviously calling long-distance, from abroad. He spoke very correct English, but he was 'foreign'; he sounded very German in fact.

'Mike,' she called across the office, 'there's a German on the line. Says he needs to talk to you urgently.'

'It's probably Schmitz from Frankfurt,' he replied, 'put him on the line.'

Michael Johnson was now a senior partner in the respectable (and respected) stockbroking company of Billings, Cooper and Parks. He had worked for them for thirty years. He worked hard. He rarely took a holiday. He was married with two children, both at university. He lived in Esher, Surrey, in a nice house, in a nice area, with his comfortable, nice, but unexciting wife, Marjorie. He was 'settled'. His life was a routine. He had nothing to look forward to.

★

25 But it was not Schmitz. 'I am so sorry to disturb you,'
the man spoke in a very formal way, 'but I do not know
what to do. I am the husband of Else, Else Kolb, from
Schleisum. I think you can remember who Else is?'

'Of course I remember Else. I did not know she had
30 married again.'

'Yes, we married ten years ago. But that is not the
reason for my call. Else is dying. The doctors say she has
three months at the most. She has been asking to see you
before she . . .' the voice broke down, 'I beg you to come
35 at once. I will send you our address by fax. Please come.
She needs you.'

There was a click. A few minutes later a fax came
through with an address, telephone and fax number in
Hagersrup, just outside Schleisum.

40 Mike called across to Tracy, 'Please cancel all my appoint-
ments for the next week. And call the travel agents. I
need a seat on a flight to Hamburg tomorrow morning.'

He sat back in his chair. Why was he doing this? He
was a careful man. He never acted carelessly. Yet he
45 could not refuse Else's request. It would cause him a lot
of trouble but . . . He began to remember Else as he had
known her – thirty-five years earlier – she had been his
first love . . . In fact his only real love.

He left the office and took the usual train home from
50 Waterloo. He thought about how he would explain all
this to Marjorie.

He arrived at Hamburg airport at eleven the following
morning. Half an hour later he had hired a car and was
driving north into Schleswig-Holstein. Schleisum is a
55 small, provincial town. It stands at the end of a long inlet
from the Baltic Sea. Nothing much happens there.
Michael had been posted to the small airbase just outside

Schleisum as part of his military service in 1956. He was
eighteen years old. Life had been boring. He often worked
at night at the radar station, checking air traffic over East   60
Germany, Poland and the Baltic. Days were spent sleeping. Then, one Sunday afternoon he had gone with his
mates to a dance at the 'Hot Club' down in town. It was
there that he had met Else. And his life had suddenly
changed.   65

He checked in to the small hotel, 'Zum Deutschen Eiche',
in the Stadtweg, the main street of the town. He remembered drinking beer there. It was small and modest but
clean. He called Hermann Doll, Else's husband. Half an
hour later, Hermann came to pick him up. He was   70
driving a new BMW. They drove out of town towards
Breckenheid, where the airbase had been. Michael remembered the many times when he had walked back to camp
after leaving Else. It was five kilometres, but, with the
thought of Else fresh in his mind, the distance had meant   75
nothing to him.

Hermann was a small man with thin sandy hair and a
wet, nervous mouth. He tried to make conversation on
the way, 'You will be shocked when you see Else. Please
do not let her see it. She has been living for this moment.'   80
They passed the airbase. It was deserted. The buildings
were empty. 'They closed it down two years ago, after
the Berlin Wall came down,' Hermann explained. In
spite of what Hermann had told him about Else, Michael
was shocked when he saw her. She lay back in the large   85
double bed in the bedroom of their suburban villa. Her
hair was grey, almost white. Her skin was transparent, like
an egg without a shell. The bones in her face stuck out
and her dark eyes were sunk deep into it. But she was still
beautiful. He sat on the bed beside her. He took her   90

hand. Hermann had left discreetly. 'You came,' she said, 'I never believed you would come.'

For the next week Michael spent every moment of the day, and sometimes the night too, with Else. Together
95 they re-lived, moment by moment, the passionate love they had shared thirty-five years earlier.

'Do you remember the first night I asked you back to the house?' she asked him.

'You mean when we went down into the cellar and sat
100 by the boiler and talked till three in the morning? How could I forget that? I had to walk back to camp in the cold!'

'And what about the night we went walking in the woods behind Schloss Gottorp? Do you remember how everything was covered in frost and how it all sparkled in
105 the moonlight?'

'What about the evening – it was summer – a very hot evening, when we had our first argument? You walked off and left me. Then we spent the next two hours desperately searching for each other. Do you remember?'

110 And so it went on. Hermann came and went, made coffee or tea, brought them food, beer or wine for Michael, gave Else her medicine, then left them alone together again. They never spoke of her illness but sometimes she would clutch Michael's hand when the pain
115 was too intense. Once or twice she made him leave her when she could not bear it any more. Then she would slip into a drugged sleep. But gradually Else seemed better now she was with Michael. So she was devastated when he told her he would be leaving the next day. He
120 had stayed a full week; he could stay no longer. He promised her he would return before . . . the end of the month. She turned her head away from him and sobbed into her pillow.

★

Hermann drove him into town early the next morning. It was the first time they had been alone together since Michael's arrival. When they stopped outside the hotel, Hermann began to talk, at first slowly and with difficulty, then more and more fluently and passionately.

'Mike – I hope I can call you Mike – I will always be grateful to you for what you have done. I am not a jealous man. I know that you are the only person she has ever really loved – no please listen to me, don't interrupt. After you left, all those years ago, she was lost. You know she married that fellow from Hamburg. She was never happy. It only lasted a year. Then she drifted in and out of relationships for years. I was lucky. I married her when she was desperate for someone who would care for her. I know that I am nothing to her compared with you, but I am grateful. I am just an insurance agent. I am not especially interesting, I know. But I have tried to make her happy. It was friendship, not love, but it was all we had. We did not have children. Perhaps it was just as well. And now she is leaving both of us.' He began to sob. Michael tried to comfort him, then left, back to Hamburg and London.

They agreed that Hermann would call as soon as the end was near. A week went by, then two, then three. Michael did not dare to call. All he could do was to wait. Two months later a letter arrived, postmarked Schleisum. It was from Else.

Dearest Mike,

I am so sorry I have not written to you or phoned you but a miracle has happened.

After you left, my health suddenly got worse. They took me to the hospital. I thought it was the end. Then, one morning I woke from the drugs and felt better – much better. Hermann was sitting beside me. Suddenly I realized what a fool I had been. I had never understood how good life has been for me.

First there was our wonderful first love together, all those years ago. I shall never forget a single moment of it, even if it broke my heart. Then you came to me when I needed you most. Without you I would have died, I know it. But when you had left, I came to understand how much I loved Hermann. I had been blind to it for so long. Suddenly, I knew. And now I am getting better! The doctors can't understand it but it's true. I have put on weight, and next week Hermann and I are going to Italy for a holiday in the sun. It is a real miracle.

Dearest Mike, I will never see you again but I will never forget you. I wish you the same happiness that I have found. Happiness is there in front of our eyes – but we don't see it. Miracles do happen.

Else.

You'll Never Know . . .

'Please enter your password,' came the recorded voice on Tony's answerphone. He did so. 'You have . . . one . . . new message. To hear your message, press one.' He thought it was one of his customers who had called after the office had closed the night before. But no. Instead of 5 a normal spoken voice, he heard part of a song. 'You'll never know just how much I love you. You'll never know just how much I care.' It was a bit old-fashioned but the message was clear. Yet who had left it? Was it a practical joke? Was it serious? If it was, who could have left a 10 message like this, without leaving a name?

Tony had been working at the agency for five years, ever since he left university. It was a small business run by the owner Fergus McDowell, a Scot with a fiery temper but a good nose for business. They were literary 15 agents. That is, they helped authors to find publishers for their work and gave them advice on contracts and other publishing matters. When they got a book published, they earned a percentage of the profits. It was a good business. But Fergus did not believe in wasting 20 money. He had a small staff. Tony looked after non-fiction titles. (Fergus handled the more glamorous fiction himself.) Fergus's daughter, Fiona, was Office Manager and his other daughter, Daphne, handled publicity and contracts. Cindy the typist was also stamp licker, photo- 25 copier, fax machine operator, coffee-maker and general dogsbody.

Tony wondered if one of these three ladies had left the mysterious message. He was a shy man who did not make friends easily, especially women friends. He had never had a proper girlfriend (though he did have a number of friends who were girls). So he was pretty certain that, if the message was not a joke, it must have been sent by one of the girls in the office. The only other possibility was Sharon Peabody. Sharon was an American economist who had invited Tony round to her flat for drinks a year back. The evening had ended in embarrassment for them both. Sharon had returned to New York and had not been heard of since. No, it could not be Sharon; she would have been much more direct.

His thoughts were interrupted by the entrance of Fergus, waving a handful of papers. Tobias Sandfurth, a leading management writer, wanted them to take over his publishing affairs. Tony would have to go over to Paris, where Tobias lived, to confirm the details. Here was the ticket. The plane would leave at 3 p.m. from Heathrow. He could read the file on the plane, have dinner with Sandfurth, tie up the deal the following morning (Fergus always pronounced it 'morrrning') and be back by the evening. Tony had learnt not to argue with Fergus, so he cleared his desk and went home to pack an overnight bag.

In the airport lounge he thought again about who might have left the message. First of all there was Fiona. She must have been about thirty. She had long chestnut coloured hair which she wore up in a twist fastened with a tortoiseshell comb. Her eyes were green and full of intelligence, but often looked sad. She was always elegantly dressed but never wore bright colours. She did not smile much but when she did you could see her inner kindness. He liked her voice too. It was a deep contralto with a very slight Scottish brogue. Her laughter was like music. He realized that he knew almost nothing about her life outside the office. He did know she had moved away from the family house after the death of their mother several months earlier. She worked hard and often stayed late at the office. He did not think she would have left such a message. He knew she liked him because she sometimes smiled at him shyly . . . but no, she would not leave messages.

Daphne was quite a different type. She had short black hair and sparkling, mischievous eyes. She was a couple of years younger than Fiona – about his age in fact. When she spoke she seemed to bubble. She always seemed to be wearing new clothes, always the latest fashion. Although she still lived at home, she spent most of her time out, going to late-night parties and discos. On weekends she went windsurfing or flew off to the Riviera or to Alpine ski resorts. She had lots of boyfriends. He sometimes wondered if she was hiding a deep unhappiness behind her frantic lifestyle. She was always very friendly to him, though. She often popped into his office for a chat. And she had the embarrassing habit of putting her hand on his shoulder or patting his arm. She'd even kissed him once at the office Christmas party; nothing serious though. He was sure that she was not interested in him. Her social life was too interesting.

That left Cindy. She was a cheeky little thing; a typical Londoner. She had an Afro hair style and usually wore mini-skirts, tight sweaters and very high heels. But she was really nice to have around. She never complained and always had something cheerful or humorous to say. Even Fergus sometimes laughed at her jokes. Until recently she had been picked up regularly by her boyfriend Nigel (Nige for short). He always wore patched jeans and a tattered leather jacket. He had safety pins through each ear and an apache hair-do, pink and green. They would zoom off on his Harley Davidson to somewhere in the East End where his fellow punks met every evening to 'have fun'. 'You only live once, don't you darling?' she used to say. She had broken up with Nige several weeks earlier. Occasionally she came to sit on Tony's desk to tell him her troubles when the others had gone home. Once he had even invited her for a drink in the pub on the corner. But he wasn't her type at all. He knew that. Anyway, she was far too young for him.

His thoughts were interrupted by the flight announcement. He picked up his bag and filed through to the waiting aircraft. The rest of his trip to Paris was a blur of activity. His discussions with Sandfurth were successful and he returned home late the next evening to his tiny basement flat in Bayswater. He felt exhausted.

Next morning he went in late. Immediately Fergus called for a report on his trip. It was mid-afternoon before he returned to his own office. There were two messages on his machine. Both were musical! 'Lithuanians and Lets do it, Let's do it, Let's fall in love', was the first. The second was 'You'll never know . . .' again. He put the phone down and decided not to think about it again. He now felt sure it was some kind of joke. It couldn't possibly be serious. He knew it could not be anyone in the office: Fiona was too serious; Daphne was too trendy; Cindy was too young.

The next few weeks passed normally. About once a week he would find a new message on his machine: 'I've never loved like this before . . .', '. . . with just a look. Could we have been in love once before? Is now the time? It seems that I know you so weeell.' He began to realize that this was no joke. Someone was really trying to tell him that they loved him. But who? Who would go to all the trouble . . .?

Two days later he returned to the office in the late afternoon after lunch with a very difficult, unpleasant author. It was a fine May day. He had walked back to clear the disagreeable memory of the man from his mind. The air was full of the perfumes of spring flowers. On his machine he found two messages. The first was the well-known 'You'll never know'. The second was, 'Meet me on the corner. Show me that you care. Meet me on the corner. I'll be waiting there.' The second message had been recorded three times, as if it was specially important.

Cindy had already gone. Daphne put her head round the door to say goodnight. She seemed to be looking for an excuse to stay but he did not look up. 'See you then. I'm just going for a quick drink at the wine bar,' she said hesitantly. She left. Fiona was still working in her office at the end of the corridor. He needed to check on a detail in a letter from the difficult author. As he was opening his door, she emerged from hers. He asked for the information, which she gave him. 'I wonder if that will satisfy him?' he asked. She looked at him with her green eyes. They looked so full of feeling in the evening light. 'You'll never know probably,' she said looking at him intensely, and walked down the stairs.

He suddenly realized what she had said. It was Fiona. She was the one! He grabbed his things, ran downstairs and caught up with her as she reached the corner. Yes, the corner. 'Meet me on the corner,' the song rang in his ears. He clumsily invited her to have a glass of wine with him at the corner wine bar. They did not see Daphne sitting in the corner when they came in. She quickly got up and left by the side entrance. That was it really. They realized very quickly that they were 'made for each other' as a song might put it. Within six months they were married.

*

165 *Our father died the following year and Tony took over. My guess is that Tony never mentioned the phone messages to Fiona. He would have been too embarrassed. So of course, she never even knew what had brought them together. Everyone thought that I, Daphne, was the bright attractive one,*
170 *but my sister Fiona got the man I loved. Why didn't I tell him myself? How could I have done that to my own sister? And they have three lovely kids now anyway. If only I'd told him I loved him! But it was too late. I went to America. I got married myself. It was a disaster. I could*
175 *never have been happy with anyone but Tony.*

Glossary and Language Practice

At Your Service

on the dot (line 16): at exactly that time.

brisk (line 21): quick.

nibbling (line 44): eating with small bites.

den (line 62): his own private room.

concession (line 73): the only way in which they conformed to what the family expected.

clue (line 98): something which would tell her what had happened to her husband.

evening off (line 99): free evening.

prise open (line 104): open with force.

swallowtail jacket (line 110): the sort of jacket worn by waiters at official dinners.

dedication (line 131): when someone gives a book to a person they often write a few words inside the book to show that they are giving it to that person. This is called a dedication.

spidery (line 145): as if a spider had crawled across the paper with ink on its legs.

a gift for . . . (line 159): a special talent; to be specially good at something.

film magnate (line 167): a very rich person who makes films or pays for them to be made.

discreetly (line 171): without making a fuss; quietly.

winked (line 178): closed one eye very quickly.

LANGUAGE PRACTICE

A

Replace the words underlined with an expression from the text based on the word(s) given in brackets. Make any necessary grammatical changes.

Example: Jack made the decision to go to America (decide).
           Jack decided to go to America.

1 He did exactly the same things at the same time every day (routine).
2 He was familiar to all the club members (know well).
3 The agency called immediately after he had left (soon).
4 Her name was Nicole but her friends called her Nicki (shorten).
5 The restaurant appeared to be empty (as if).
6 He thought he might find the evidence he was looking for (perhaps).
7 Compared with this, his own troubles were negligible (by comparison).
8 Mike and his wife are both interested in the same things (share).
9 Entry to the club was prohibited to non-members (allowed).
10 This was the first time he had ever used a word-processor (never).

B

Supply the missing words. In each case, the first letter of the missing word is given. All these expressions are taken from the text.

1 She used to walk r_____ the c_____ to the pub.
2 He had been d_____ research i_____ the breeding habits of mice.
3 He was very old so everyone was u_____ t_____ his funny ways.
4 I've decided to s_____ the summer in Crete.

5 It wasn't easy. It t_____ him almost an h_____ to finish it.
6 The detective began to l_____ t_____ the letters to see if they contained anything incriminating.
7 I am sorry, but I have d_____ to sack you.
8 The child h_____ o_____ its hands towards me.
9 The car came t_____ a h_____ in front of the bank.
10 His secretary m_____ s_____ no one interrupted his work.

C

Questions for discussion.

1 Why do you think Eloise and Edouard got married?
2 What do you think Eloise looked like? Describe her in detail.
3 What satisfactions do you think Edouard gets from his new life? Make a list of points for and against his old life, and his new life.

Campbell's Crossing

GLOSSARY

crofts (line 8): small mountain farms in Scotland.
capsized (line 13): turned upside-down in the water.
all the heads would turn (line 36): everyone would turn to look at her.
rivalry (line 39): when two people want the same thing, and only one of them can have it.
took to (line 43): got into the habit of.
kirk (Scottish word) (line 46): church.
sulked (line 46): sulking is when we show our displeasure by refusing to smile or talk.
proposed to her (line 59): asked her to marry him.
glen (Scottish word) (line 61): mountain valley.
ceilidh (Scottish word, pronounced 'kay-lee') (line 83): music/dancing party where everyone joins in.

fiddle (line 86): violin.
remote (line 108): isolated.
commuted (line 122): travelled a long way to and from work.
subsiding (line 133): going down, getting lower.
the night wore on (line 151) it got later and later.
hoar frost (line 159): white crystals of ice.
hauled up (line 161): pulled up.
debris (line 169): rubbish in the river, such as tree branches, etc.

LANGUAGE PRACTICE·

A

Replace the words underlined with an expression from the text based on the word(s) given in brackets. Make any necessary grammatical changes.

Example: <u>The rain continued without a break</u> until April (went on).

It went on raining until April.

1 <u>Crossing</u> the mountains was just possible but very dangerous (it/get across).
2 <u>No one could resist the sight of her</u> when she walked by (heads turn).
3 The two women began to <u>compete more and more aggressively</u> for promoton (rivalry between).
4 Maggie <u>wrote regularly to inform us of</u> events in the village (keep up to date).
5 When the holidays were over, Tom <u>did not come home from</u> France (stay on).
6 For the next five years her parents saw <u>no more of her</u> (last).
7 He had <u>not wanted to speak</u> to her (unwillingly).
8 It felt almost <u>as if nothing had changed since they were kids</u> (old times).
9 Peter <u>would not listen to anyone, and went</u> into the forest (insist).
10 <u>It was impossible for</u> Tim <u>to desert</u> Sandy (leave alone).

B

Supply the missing words. In each case, the first letter of the missing word is given. All these expressions are taken from the text.

1 The cattle were w_____ a_____ by the flood waters.
2 We all g_____ u_____ together and went to the same school.
3 She was so striking – I was h_____ in l_____ with her.
4 They did everything together; they were i_____.
5 Let me bring you u_____ t_____ d_____ with all the latest gossip.
6 The offer was so good that I c_____ r_____ it.
7 People are funny. You never know what g_____ o_____ in their h_____.
8 When he left her, she tried to h_____ her f_____ but everyone could see how upset she was.
9 They didn't have much money. But m_____ isn't e_____, is it?
10 Now the war is over, everything is b_____ to n_____ again.

C

Questions for discussion.

1 Why do you think Colin's footsteps led up to the window and then back into the water? What happened?
2 How would you have felt if you were Angus or Fiona? Why?
3 What do you think became of Fiona and Angus afterwards?
4 Do you know of any other love stories which end in tragedy?

Keep It Dark

GLOSSARY

Keep it dark (title): Don't tell anyone.
mind's eye (line 16): visual memory.
a crawl (line 28): very slow speed.

cut off (line 35): blocked the light from the sun.

make out (line 38): see.

evaporated (line 41): gone.

loomed up (line 44): suddenly became visible.

wisps (line 48): thin mist, like hair.

illusion (line 50): something which is not really there but which
    seems to be there.

wound (line 57): twisted and turned.

huddling (line 59): sheltering.

crippled (line 61): permanently deformed.

broke away (line 64): fell off.

sheer instinct (line 65): acting without thinking; a reflex action.

nestled (line 71): like an egg in a nest.

jangled (line 80): made a loud metallic noise.

eerie (line 82): strange, unearthly, ghostly.

a living soul (line 84): a person.

screech (line 88): the noise that car tyres make when you put the
    brakes on suddenly.

nickname (line 109): short name that your friends give you.

chilly (line 114): cold.

whacked (line 115): very tired.

plumbing (line 119): the water pipes.

in stages (line 124): one part after another; not all at once.

splattered (line 162): splashed in spots.

rumble (line 174): the noise a heavy object makes when it rolls
    along.

imploring (line 180): begging.

LANGUAGE PRACTICE

A

*Replace the words underlined with an expression from the text
based on the word given in brackets. Make any necessary grammatical changes.*

Example: I <u>am not in a hurry</u> (time).
          I have plenty of time.

  1 <u>Visibility was down to</u> a few yards (see).

2 I <u>was filled with loneliness and confusion</u> (feel).
3 I put my foot on the brake <u>without thinking</u> (instinct).
4 It had <u>almost hit me</u> (miss).
5 <u>I was alone</u> in the shop (customer).
6 <u>The</u> room you have been <u>allocated</u> is number 16 (put).
7 <u>It would be nice to have</u> a hot bath (welcome).
8 <u>My</u> holiday was <u>very disturbed</u> (quiet).
9 I <u>plucked up</u> my courage and asked her to marry me (hands).
10 Josephine <u>claims that</u> I fell asleep (According . . .).

B

Supply the missing words. In each case, the first letter of the missing word is given. All these expressions are taken from the text.

1 There was no hurry. I h_____ the whole a_____ to write the report.
2 We decided to s_____ f_____ a rest.
3 The snow had c_____ o_____ the railway line to the capital.
4 She was terrified. She c_____ o_____ 'Help!'
5 The s_____ you learn to behave, the b_____.
6 There's plenty to eat and drink. Please h_____ y_____.
7 The telephone ringing w_____ me u_____.
8 It was very dangerous. I h_____ my b_____ until the snake slithered away.
9 The explosion was so loud that my e_____ were r_____.
10 You've been travelling all day. You m_____ b_____ w_____.

C

Questions for discussion.

1 How do you explain what happened that night?
2 What do you think Sphinx told Clive the next morning?
3 Have you had any experiences similar to this one? Do you know anyone who has?

A Real Dark Horse

GLOSSARY

a wreath (line 1): flowers and leaves woven together into a circle-shape. Usually given as a mark of respect at funerals.

bruised (line 4): the dark mark we get on our skin if it is hit by something.

crouched (line 8): the houses were low, near the earth, like animals with their legs bent down.

mine-tips (line 10): coal mines usually have waste tips next to them. These are like artificial hills of unwanted rock and dust.

crêpe (line 12): a kind of very thin, light fabric.

left (line 26): he had given it to her in his will when he died.

broker (line 29): a man who deals in finance: stocks, shares, bonds, etc.

baggy (line 41): too big for him; not well pressed.

taken over (line 50): when one company buys another, they 'take it over'.

chores (line 52): boring jobs around the house.

cortège (line 71): the funeral procession, with the coffin.

the hearse (line 82): the special car which transports the coffin to the graveyard.

sleet (line 84): half rain, half snow.

cobbles (line 85): small stone blocks used to pave a street.

vault (line 92): an underground room or space which can be sealed. Coffins are sealed in a funeral vault and there are also bank vaults, where we can store our money, etc.

grog (line 98): a mixture of rum (or other spirits), water, sugar and spices. It is usually served hot.

ladling (line 99): using a big spoon (ladle) to put the soup in the plates.

pagan (line 102): before Christianity came to Europe, people had other religions called 'pagan'.

butler (line 104): the chief male servant in a household.

notaire (French word) (line 124): a kind of lawyer.

mothballs (line 124): chemical balls with a strong smell of camphor which are used to keep moths away from clothes stored in cupboards.

plump (line 135): quite fat.

assets (line 139): the things a person owns.

ninny (line 143): idiot.

snarled (line 144): like an angry dog when it bares its teeth.

flushed (line 162): a red face.

confidence trickster (line 163): someone who cheats people out of their money.

You jerk (line 163): a term of abuse, like 'You rat!'

a real dark horse (line 186): someone who seems very quiet on the surface but who is very interesting underneath.

a lingering kiss (line 188): a kiss that lasted a long time.

LANGUAGE PRACTICE

A

Replace the words underlined with an expression from the text based on the word(s) given in brackets. Make any necessary grammatical changes.

Example: I was barely acquainted with Denise (know well).
I had not known Denise well.

1 All around the castle were the castle grounds (stand/own).
2 I had learnt everything I knew about Gustave from other people (what/know/come from).
3 She remained a widow (marry).
4 There was nothing special about Humphrey (ordinary).
5 Apparently he was especially talented when it came to money (gift).
6 He was naturally polite, unlike his customers, who were rude (contrasted).
7 We were expecting the doctor at six to give the injections (due).
8 There was an atmosphere of evil in the room (feel/air).
9 Everything else I own is in the bank (assets).
10 I was the person she consulted whenever she had problems (Each time/come to).

B

*Supply the missing words. In each case, the first letter of the
missing word is given. All these expressions are taken from the
text.*

1 I couldn't concentrate because people kept on c_____
i_____ and o_____.
2 Now that your father has died, it is my d_____ to
l_____ a_____ you.
3 He liked eating and drinking. He certainly k_____ how
to e_____ life.
4 His company was t_____ o_____ by a multi-national
corporation.
5 Frank s_____ a lot of t_____ in the garden.
6 After the opera, we m_____ our w_____ back to the
hotel.
7 They cooperate very well; they really w_____ as a
t_____.
8 You've told us the bad news; now w_____ a_____ the
good news?
9 He enjoyed our embarrassment. A s_____ p_____
around his l_____ as he spoke.
10 Now that I've retired, I intend to m_____ the m_____
of my life.

C

Questions for discussion.

1 Do you know anyone who is a 'dark horse'? Tell someone
about him/her.
2 Why do you think Hortense and Leopold came together in
the first place? And why did they stay together for so
long?
3 Do you know of any cases where there has been a dispute
over the will of a family member?
4 What do you think Michel and Ginette will do now?

Man Proposes . . .

GLOSSARY

sipped (line 1): drank small amounts at a time.

blend (line 5): mixture.

a string of (line 13): a long list of.

consultancies (line 14): many companies pay private experts (consultants) to write reports for them.

'elder statesman' (line 14): a respected senior person.

the seating plan (line 22): at formal dinners and receptions there are cards on every table with the names of the people who are to sit in those places.

haggard (line 29): tired-looking.

figures to balance (line 30): adding up what the company has spent and comparing it with what it has earned.

detached (line 42): unemotional.

mortgage (line 45): money we borrow to buy a house.

dappled (line 58): patches of light and shade.

shambled (line 67): walked clumsily.

clutched (line 68): held tightly.

lolled to one side (line 70): hung in a loose, unsupported way.

slack (line 70): loose.

slobbered (line 76): saliva ran out of her mouth noisily.

tugged (line 85): pulled.

muttered (line 91): talked indistinctly.

twit (line 106): fool.

'see them off to a good start' (line 114): give them money to help them start their marriage.

zebra crossing (line 127): black and white stripes painted across a road so that people can cross safely. Cars are supposed to stop at a zebra crossing to allow people to cross.

thump (line 128): a loud, dull noise.

in lieu of notice (line 136): When people lose their jobs, the employer usually gives them notice: are told to leave one month or more later. Sometimes the employer pays them their wages for this time to leave immediately. This is 'in lieu of notice'.

LANGUAGE PRACTICE

A

Replace the words underlined with an expression from the text based on the word(s) given in brackets. Make any necessary grammatical changes.

Example: His new gardener <u>was really good at growing</u> roses (understand about).

His new gardener really understood about roses.

1 He joined the navy as a boy and <u>became</u> Admiral of the Fleet (work/ranks).
2 There are still <u>a few details to be agreed in</u> the contract (finalize).
3 Jason tried <u>all sorts of jobs but none of them</u> succeeded (whatever).
4 When she was demoted, they offered her a job in South America <u>as a way of making her feel better</u> (soften blow).
5 I have <u>had</u> the subject <u>under close observation</u> (keep eye).
6 If they don't arrive soon, <u>we'll certainly be late</u> for the party (in time).
7 I'm going to tell you something – <u>but please don't tell anyone else</u> (in confidence).
8 <u>He had expected</u> the interview <u>to be much more difficult</u> (feared).
9 He knew he had to find a way of stopping people from <u>hearing about the scandal</u> (keep quiet).
10 Jane <u>couldn't see the end of</u> the queue for tickets (as far as).

B

Supply the missing words. In each case, the first letter of the missing word is given. All these expressions are taken from the text.

1 This tea is very hot; you'd better s_____ it carefully.
2 How do you like my new car? It's a Rolls-Royce. Only the b_____ is g_____ e_____ you know.
3 I'll be late home tonight. I've got a lot of work to do so I'm s_____ o_____ until I finish it.

4 I can't let you into the factory without a pass. It's m_____ than my j_____ is w_____.

5 I've lost my job, my house, my family ... everything. W_____ w_____ b_____ of me?

6 Mrs Wilkins has popped out to the shops. I'm k_____ an e_____ on her kids till she gets back.

7 After my accident people started to look at me strangely. At first I was upset, but I'm u_____ t_____ i_____ by now.

8 The dog suddenly jumped over the fence and r_____ a_____ the field.

9 I don't like the new secretary so I'm going to g_____ r_____ of her.

10 When Daren told me he'd broken up with Sadie I heaved a s_____ of r_____.

C

Questions for discussion.

1 Who do you think is the most guilty person in the story? If you were a judge, what punishment would you give?

2 Imagine you have to interview each of the characters after this tragedy, in order to write a newspaper article. Which questions would you ask them?

3 Write down a list of adjectives which best describe each of the four main characters, e.g. Bruce Nesbitt – greedy, self-satisfied, etc.

Paul

GLOSSARY

shivered (line 9): shook with cold.
with a clear conscience (line 13): he would not feel guilty about it.
dingy (line 14): dark and not very clean.
peered (line 15): he had to look very hard in order to see anything.

gasping (line 38): as if she could not breathe easily.

puffy (line 39): the flesh was blown up like a balloon.

neglected (line 40): not well cared for.

stacks (line 41): piles; heaps.

waxed (line 45): polished.

drily (line 58): in a bitter way.

irony (line 58): he was mocking himself when he said, 'It's a record.'

all the ins and outs (line 63): all the details; all the information.

courtship (line 69): when they were in love, before they were married.

taken the floor (line 73): gone on to the dance floor.

on the point of tears (line 94): as if she was about to cry.

Protestant (line 96): one of the main branches of Christianity – Catholics are another main branch.

crawled (line 130): gone very slowly.

parched (line 131): very dry.

hunks (line 132): large pieces.

clinking (line 136): the noise ice makes in a glass.

oozed (line 140): when a liquid comes out slowly, it oozes.

dye (line 140): a substance which colours things. For example, you can dye a white dress blue.

shutters (line 148): wooden or metal flaps which can be opened or closed to cover a window to keep out the sunlight.

zoomed (line 152): went very fast.

lazed (line 155): did not do anything.

committed suicide (line 164): killed himself.

grieving (line 174): feeling very sad about something.

glued (line 191): stuck.

perspired (line 206): sweated.

profusely (line 206): a lot.

tepid (line 208): not hot, not cold, but a little warm.

mellow (line 211): ripe.

LANGUAGE PRACTICE

A

Replace the words underlined with an expression from the text based on the word(s) given in brackets. Make any necessary grammatical changes.

Example: It was <u>not very difficult</u> to find the street again (easy).

It was easy enough to find the street again.

1 He did not recognize the woman <u>immediately</u> (seconds).
2 He was <u>certain that</u> the child was his son (definitely).
3 There was <u>only</u> an old car in the garage (except).
4 The old man's face was completely <u>without expression</u> (show/emotion).
5 <u>My husband is French</u> (married).
6 <u>If you don't</u> pay me 100 francs, you can't come in (otherwise).
7 Jack now seemed to be <u>someone else</u> (same person).
8 The coffee <u>did not smell</u> the same (aroma).
9 He left <u>with an apology</u> (make excuse).
10 She <u>had been terribly proud</u> of her garden (pride).

B

Supply the missing words. In each case, the first letter of the missing word is given. All these expressions are taken from the text.

1 I p_____ the lorry next to the cemetery.
2 Hello. Yes. Speaking. What c_____ I d_____ f_____ you?
3 I think he'd just g_____ o_____ of b_____. He looked so sleepy.
4 My uncle s_____ in the police force for 25 years.
5 He had to r_____ when he was sixty.
6 I've had a bad back-ache, so I've been o_____ s_____ for the past two days.
7 Peter met Jane at a dance. They were e_____ within a week. They m_____ six months later.

8 Come quickly! There's an u_____ t_____ c_____
for you.

9 We didn't know each other very well but during our climb-
ing holiday we became c_____ f_____.

10 He drove the car down the hill at b_____ s_____. I
was so frightened.

C

Questions for discussion.

1 Have you ever had an experience like this one – where you
go back to a place you have good memories of from many
years before? Tell someone about it.

2 We are not told much about the narrator. Make a list of the
things the story *does* tell us about him. Then try to imagine
what kind of person he is. Can you form a picture of what
he looks like? Talk about this to someone else to see if you
agree.

3 Try to imagine what the Portinis' life is like. What is
their daily routine? What do they talk about in the
evenings?

Cold Comfort

GLOSSARY

lead (line 7): a very heavy metal, used for pipes, roofing, etc.

hanging about (line 8): waiting in the street aimlessly.

scavenging (line 9): looking for things other people have thrown
away.

corpse (line 13): a dead body.

gingerly (line 14): very carefully, in order not to hurt himself.

wedged (line 17): stuck.

snake out (line 21): moving swiftly, like a snake.

rouse (line 26): wake up.

furtively (line 28): secretively, as if he had something to hide.

out of work (line 40): unemployed; without a job.

from hand to mouth (line 49): from one moment to the next, with no security.

let alone (line 56): certainly not enough for a rail fare.

scruffy (line 83): untidy.

threadbare (line 87): worn out, thin cloth.

to mug (line 114): beat him and steal his money.

inside information (line 122): information ordinary people do not have.

lying well back (line 145): well behind.

a whole length (line 150): the length of a horse.

betting slip (line 158): the receipt to prove he had made the bet.

LANGUAGE PRACTICE

A

Replace the words underlined with an expression from the text based on the word(s) given in brackets. Make any necessary grammatical changes.

Example: She realized that the bag was her own (belong).
             She realized that the bag belonged to her.

1 She could not understand why he had written to her (no idea).
2 My brother has not had a job for three years (out of work).
3 She thought it would be preferable to work on her own (better off).
4 He read the letter. It announced that he had won the biggest prize (hit).
5 They started to have a friendly chat with Mac (fall).
6 If you buy me a meal, I'll tell you where he is (price).
7 According to his calculations, he had won £100 (work out).
8 They had left the restaurant quietly without telling him (slip).
9 He felt the beginnings of hunger (begin).
10 Jim was informed by his best friend that his mother was seriously ill (tell).

B

Supply the missing words. In each case, the first letter of the missing word is given. All these expressions are taken from the text.

1 He f_____ the camera on the tiger's eyes.
2 There was something wrong going on; she felt it in her b_____.
3 The letter was screwed into a ball. He quickly tried to s_____ it out, so that he could read it.
4 The thief g_____ the old lady's bag and ran off.
5 He is still out of work but he has a t_____ job as a waiter.
6 Can you advise me? I want to i_____ my money as wisely as I can.
7 The crowds were p_____ out of the football stadium.
8 While he was shaving, he looked at his r_____ in the bathroom mirror, and wondered.
9 We were feeling hungry so we went into the n_____ café for a snack.
10 The police w_____ me not to drink and drive.

C

Questions for discussion.

1 What do you think 'really' happened in the story?
2 Now you have read the story, what advice would you give to Ken?
3 Do you know of anyone who has been cheated of their money? Has it ever happened to you?

Alfred's Enigmatic Smile

GLOSSARY

enigmatic (title): difficult to interpret.
stick-in-the-mud (line 5): a humorous way of referring to someone who never leaves his home village.

tinted (line 13): coloured.

misty (line 13): not very clear.

drab (line 19): dull, uninteresting.

faded (line 19): when we put brightly coloured clothes in the sun they become faded, not so bright.

clasped (line 25): held tightly together.

mask (line 38): usually something we wear over our face, to hide it.

flabby (line 43): fat, soft.

putty (line 46): a grey paste used to hold window panes in place.

on purpose (line 55): intentionally

undertaking (line 58): an undertaker is someone who arranges for the burial of dead people.

trudge (line 74): to walk in a heavy, tired way.

mustn't grumble (line 79): it means 'Things are not so bad for me.'

ragamuffin (line 80): an untidy boy; usually one who gets into trouble.

green fingers (line 104): someone who is good at gardening is said to have 'green fingers'.

coma (line 115): state of unconsciousness.

slurred (line 117): speech which is not clear.

gangrene (line 119): very serious infection in a limb, usually the foot or leg.

amputated (line 119): cut off.

weather these storms (line 125): get over these difficulties.

bellow (line 151): shout loud, like a bull or a cow.

ajar (line 155): half-open.

secateurs (line 171): something like scissors, used for cutting flowers or plants.

come out of it (line 178): recover; regain consciousness.

coroner (line 179): the official who has to certify the cause of death.

autopsy (line 180): the medical examination carried out on dead bodies to find out the cause of death.

a blur (line 185): vague, indistinct.

severed (line 192): cut off.

tipped off (line 195): give information to someone. 'The police were tipped off about the bank robbery.'

LANGUAGE PRACTICE

A

Replace the words underlined with an expression from the text based on the word(s) given in brackets. Make any necessary grammatical changes.

Example: He <u>had not changed very much</u> (remember).
             He looked almost as I remembered him.

1 I'm <u>not surprised that you don't like it</u> (blame).
2 When she spoke, <u>I remembered</u> everything that had happened (bring back).
3 He <u>earns his living</u> by selling old newspapers (make).
4 She tried to <u>encourage him to talk to her</u> (draw).
5 Her bad temper <u>got worse</u> after the accident (improve).
6 I walked away <u>quietly</u> so that grandfather would not wake up (tip-toe).
7 This time he did not <u>regain consciousness</u> (come out).
8 Do you know who <u>gave the information to</u> the police (tip off)?
9 My uncle is <u>making a good recovery after</u> his operation (get over).
10 When I was a kid, the Smiths <u>were neighbours of ours</u> (next door).

B

Supply the missing words. In each case, the first letter of the missing word is given. All these expressions are taken from the text.

1 When he invited me to his table, I sh_____ my h_____.
2 We to live n_____ d_____ to the Feavers.
3 I'm very angry. I'll never s_____ to y_____ again.

4 I like your hat. It's j_____ l_____ the one I used to wear.

5 Ouch! That hurts. I think you're doing it o_____ p_____.

6 It's very noisy in here but I've got u_____ t_____ it now.

7 I was very upset at the time but I'm g_____ o_____ it now.

8 Because he was such a good cook, they put him i_____ c_____ of the kitchen.

9 Why should I p_____ u_____ with your bad temper?

10 It's too painful. I c_____ s_____ it any longer.

C

Questions for discussion.

1 Find all the proverbs or sayings that Alfred uses. Can you guess their meanings? If not look them up. Do you have similar proverbs in your language?

2 Why do you think the coroner became suspicious of Alfred?

3 What would you have done if you had seen and heard what the boy witnessed?

Esivi

GLOSSARY

colleague (line 3): a person you work with.

bachelor (line 8): a man who is not married. ('Spinster' is the equivalent word for a woman.)

insomnia (line 16): when you cannot sleep at night, you have insomnia.

garbage (line 27): rubbish and household waste.

secluded (line 40): quiet, away from the centre of activity.

vibrancy (line 45): excitement and energy.

run-down (line 50): uncared for, shabby.

stroll (line 57): to walk slowly for pleasure.

93

surf (line 61): when the very big waves break on the shore, they form the surf.

Mammy-truck (line 90): a lorry with seats in for passengers. A popular form of cheap transport in West Africa.

okra (line 95): a tropical vegetable (ladies' fingers).

quivering (line 117): shaking.

coup (d'état) (line 120): when a group of people overthrows the government, usually by force.

wanted persons (line 125): a list of people the government wants to arrest.

stunned (line 152): when we are stunned, we feel as if we have been hit on the head. We are so shocked that we cannot think straight.

valiant (line 155): brave.

tyrannical (line 156): acting in a dictatorial way, oppressing the people.

despotic (line 157): see tyrranical.

corrupt (line 159): rotten. Corrupt people take money from others in exchange for favours, etc.

rounded up (line 166): arrested.

corpses (line 170): dead bodies.

expelled (line 174): forced to leave.

LANGUAGE PRACTICE

A

Replace the words underlined with an expression from the text based on the word given in brackets. Make any necessary grammatical changes.

Example: There is something I must explain to you (owe).
            I owe you an explanation.

1 We were reasonably well acquainted (knew).
2 There were cheering crowds all along the route (line).
3 He worked very hard but he only just made enough to live on (scratch).
4 You do not have to teach many hours in this job (demanding).

5 We used to <u>tell each other</u> jokes (exchange).
6 The guest <u>kept staring at</u> the picture (eyes).
7 <u>I did not have the opportunity</u> to ask my question (chance).
8 The protesters were <u>imprisoned</u> by the government (jail).
9 The party <u>stripped the old guard of their membership</u> (expel).
10 I shall <u>always remember</u> her smile (forget).

B

Supply the missing words. In each case, the first letter(s) of the missing word is (are) given. All these expressions are taken from the text.

1 I live right o_____ the school.
2 Her parents couldn't s_____ h_____ from marrying him.
3 They've i_____ us o_____ for dinner.
4 Most people were quite happy. Only a m_____ was discontented.
5 He hates to s_____ a_____ waiting for people.
6 I have n_____ f_____ how beautiful she was.
7 They were very kind. They invited me in and made me feel a_____ h_____.
8 He's greedy. He always gr_____ e_____ for himself.
9 I c_____ t_____ y_____ how difficult it was to find you.
10 After I'd finished packing, they drove me s_____ to the station.

C

Questions for discussion.

1 Imagine you are Dr Hanson. What questions would you want to ask David?
2 What do you think David will do, now that he has found his daughter?
3 Do you think David and Esivi would have been happy together if they had married?

The Man Who Talked to Trees

GLOSSARY

hero (line 5): a brave man.

identical (line 8): exactly the same.

piercing (line 10): very intense eyes, which seem to look inside you.

erect (line 11): standing up straight.

to bully (line 15): when someone bigger or older hits or torments someone smaller or younger. A bully (noun).

retreating (line 21): running away after a defeat in battle.

tending (line 24): looking after.

oak, beech, chestnut (line 28): types of trees.

timber (line 29): another word for trees or wood when we think of it being used for building, etc.

rotation (line 32): taking turns, one after the other. One year they would cut trees from one part of the forest; the next year they would cut in a different place.

insult (line 37): for example, if you call someone an idiot, it is an insult.

spare time (line 42): free time.

glazed (line 45): shining with a hard surface. We glaze pottery.

blur (line 56): something you cannot see clearly.

sap (line 58): the juice inside a tree.

thugs (line 84): criminals who attack people.

vat (line 92): a big container into which we put grapes/wine, or whisky, or chemicals while they are being processed.

fumes (line 94): gases.

quenching (line 116): satisfying your thirst.

hermit (line 135): usually a religious man who lives alone.

inheritance (line 151): when someone dies their property is given to someone else. This is an inheritance.

shuddered (line 175): shook violently.

a short cut (line 184): a quick way to get from one place to the next.

LANGUAGE PRACTICE

A

Replace the words underlined with an expression from the text based on the word(s) given in brackets. Make any necessary grammatical changes.

Example: They were <u>inseparable</u> (together).
They were always together.

1 Strangers could not tell <u>the difference between them</u> (apart).
2 He <u>took advantage of</u> his strength to bully her (use).
3 <u>What he wanted most</u> was to become Prime Minister (ambition).
4 He arrived <u>miraculously</u> just when they were in danger (magic).
5 People <u>talked about</u> his strange habits (rumours).
6 The pain <u>was too much for him</u> (bear).
7 Because he was such a violent man, <u>nobody interfered with him</u> (leave alone).
8 The manager <u>gave him a much better job</u> (promote).
9 <u>Everybody felt very sorry</u> when he left the village (regret).
10 Jack left the job <u>soon afterwards</u> (not long).

B

Supply the missing words. In each case, the first letter of the missing word is given. All these expressions are taken from the text.

1 He managed to e＿＿＿＿ from prison.
2 When Len was a boy, he broke some windows and g＿＿＿＿ i＿＿＿＿ t＿＿＿＿.
3 Mickey liked joking; he was always p＿＿＿＿ t＿＿＿＿ on people.
4 The town was completely d＿＿＿＿ during the war.
5 Please be careful with that Chinese vase. It is very v＿＿＿＿.
6 When we arrived for the party, they threw tomatoes at us. It was an i＿＿＿＿.

97

7 The old man looked ill. He was s_____ from side to side; I thought he was going to fall down.

8 Finally we found the lost dog. It was c_____ in the corner of the garage.

9 My sister died suddenly last year of a h_____ a_____.

10 We were in a hurry, so we took a s_____ c_____ across the fields.

C

Questions for discussion.

1 Both brothers died at exactly the same time. How do you explain this?

2 If you could ask Torbash and Milmaq three questions each, what would you ask them?

3 Do you know any twins? Is it true that there is something special about the way twins communicate with each other?

Miracles Do Happen

GLOSSARY

stockbroking company (line 17): a company dealing in financial business and investments on the stock market.

she has three months at the most (line 33): she will die within three months.

had been posted (line 57): had been sent.

mates (line 63): friends, colleagues.

transparent (line 87): it was so thin that you could see through it.

discreetly (line 91): quietly and tactfully, so as not to disturb anyone.

clutch (line 114): grab hard.

devastated (line 118): very upset and unhappy.

sobbed (line 122): cried, wept.

just as well (line 142): perhaps it was better.

LANGUAGE PRACTICE

A

Replace the words underlined with an expression from the text based on the word(s) given in brackets. Make any necessary grammatical changes.

Example: Hello. <u>What</u> can I <u>do for</u> you? (help).
            Hello. How can I help you?

1 Mervyn, <u>there's someone calling you from Italy</u> (Italian/line).
2 His <u>future</u> life was <u>completely predictable</u> (look forward).
3 But <u>I am calling you about something completely different</u> (not/reason).
4 Carl <u>always thought before he</u> acted (never/carelessly).
5 <u>You will find George's appearance shocking</u> (see/shock).
6 <u>It took us</u> the next two hours <u>to find</u> our way out of the city (spend/search).
7 His marriage <u>was never mentioned</u> (they/speak).
8 <u>He thinks the world of you and</u> nothing <u>of me</u> (compare/to him).
9 <u>It may be that</u> this was preferable (as well).
10 He could do <u>nothing but</u> sleep (all/do).

B

Supply the missing words. In each case, the first letter of the missing word is given. All these expressions are taken from the text.

1 I'm sorry but it's five o'clock. I'm i_____ a h_____ to leave.
2 Jack, your mother's o_____ the l_____ from London.
3 Every day I get up at the same time, I do the same things, eat the same food – it's just the same old boring r_____.
4 If you disobey his orders, it will c_____ you a lot of t_____.
5 This is a very boring town. N_____ m_____ happens here.

99

6 Though we had nothing to say to each other, he kept on trying to m_____ c_____ with me.

7 When the firm was taken over, they cl_____ d_____ the factory.

8 We were separated in the crowd, and couldn't find e_____ o_____.

9 We broke up in 1970. Perhaps it was j_____ a_____ well.

10 I didn't have her phone number, so all I c_____ d_____ was to wait.

C

Questions for discussion.

1 Do you know of anyone who has suddenly behaved irrationally after years of routine living?

2 How many miracles do you think there were in the story?

3 Do you think Else's letter will cause a change in Mike's life? How?

4 Do you know of any cases where a very sick person has experienced a sudden, miraculous cure? How do you explain it?

5 'People who love each other do not always marry. People who marry do not always love each other.' Do you agree?

You'll Never Know . . .

GLOSSARY

a practical joke (line 9): a trick one person plays on another to make them look foolish.

with a fiery temper (line 14): someone who gets angry very quickly.

a good nose for business (line 15): a good business sense.

a percentage of the profits (line 19): for example, if the author earned 2000 pounds, Fergus would get perhaps 10%, that is 200 pounds.

dogsbody (line 27): the person who does all the jobs no one else wants to do.

tie up the deal (line 48): complete the agreement and sign the contract.

brogue (line 61): accent.

bubble (line 73): like a pot boiling.

frantic (line 80): madly active.

patting (line 83): touching with soft, gentle 'hits' of the hand.

a cheeky little thing (line 87): someone with no respect for authority.

picked up (line 93): collected.

Harley Davidson (line 97): a type of motorbike.

a blur of activity (line 108): things happened so fast that they all merged into each other.

trendy (line 122): fashionable; following the latest trend.

emerged (line 149): came out of.

took over (line 165): took control of the business.

LANGUAGE PRACTICE

A

Replace the words underlined with an expression from the text based on the word(s) given in brackets. Make any necessary grammatical changes.

Example: <u>It was not</u> a recorded message <u>but</u> part of a song (instead of).

Instead of a recorded message, it was part of a song.

1 He <u>started working for Jacksons as soon as</u> he left school (ever since).
2 James <u>was a very thrifty man</u> (waste money).
3 Overseas sales <u>were</u> Max's <u>responsibility</u> (look after).
4 I guess she <u>was</u> about fifty years old at the time (must be).
5 Jamie is <u>a</u> really good <u>colleague</u> (have around).
6 She had <u>even occasionally managed to make Jackson laugh</u> at her jokes (Even Jackson).
7 <u>Her relationship</u> with Kim <u>had come to an end</u> a few weeks before (break up).

8 The significance of his decision suddenly <u>dawned on me</u> (realize).

9 <u>No one else</u> but Jack could <u>ever have made me</u> happy (I . . . never).

10 He <u>resolved to put her out of his mind for good</u> (not think).

B

Supply the missing words. In each case, the first letter of the missing word is given. All these expressions are taken from the text.

1 A lot of people ask for our a_____ on financial matters.

2 Let's have a sandwich; I don't believe in w_____ m_____ on restaurants.

3 I don't go out much, so I don't meet many people. So I don't m_____ f_____ very easily.

4 Hi! Why don't you c_____ r_____ to my flat for a d_____?

5 I'm getting old. I'd like you to t_____ o_____ my business affairs.

6 I m_____ a_____ from home after my father died.

7 My wife is a c_____ of y_____ younger than me.

8 Are you busy? Do you mind if I p_____ i_____ for a few minutes?

9 They went out together several times; but it was n_____ s_____ though.

10 I believe in enjoying myself. You only l_____ o_____ after all.

C

Questions for discussion.

1 What is the key sentence in the story? Why?

2 If you had to describe the narrator of the story to someone else, what would you say about him?

3 Do you think Tony would have been happy if he'd married Daphne? Why?

4 Have you heard of any other cases where people got married by coincidence in this way?